Electrical Installation Practice
Book I

Electrical Installation Practice Book I

Fourth edition

H. A. Miller

Revised by
R. D. Puckering, LCG, BEd
Paddington College

BSP PROFESSIONAL BOOKS
OXFORD LONDON EDINBURGH
BOSTON MELBOURNE

First published 1989

British Library
Cataloguing in Publication Data
Puckering, R. D.
  Electrical installation practice.
  Bk. 1
  1. Electrical equipment.   Installation
  I. Title
  621.31′042

ISBN 0–632–02539–5

BSP Professional Books
A division of Blackwell Scientific
  Publications Ltd
Editorial Offices:
Osney Mead, Oxford OX2 0EL
  (Orders: Tel. 0865 240201)
8 John Street, London WC1N 2ES
23 Ainslie Place, Edinburgh EH3 6AJ
3 Cambridge Center, Suite 208, Cambridge,
  MA 02142, USA
107 Barry Street, Carlton, Victoria 3053,
  Australia

Set by Setrite Typesetters Ltd

Printed and bound in Great Britain by
  Mackays of Chatham, PLC,
  Chatham, Kent.

Contents

Preface

This well-known series of books on the craft practice aspects of electrical installation work has been updated to meet the new emphasis on practical competence. The books cover installation practice, associated craft theory, safe working practice, and a study of the electrical industries.

The purpose of Book 1 is to introduce students to the electricity industry, and to the basic practical skills needed in installation work. It takes you through the syllabus of City and Guilds course 236 step-by-step, and covers your first year in learning electrical installation practice.

The first step in any practical work is to learn how to work safely and prevent accidents. This book not only explains the law and the regulations, but gives practical examples learnt from long experience, and checklists of dos and don'ts, and what to do when an accident happens.

Following chapters explain electrical supplies, and the installation of wiring systems and lighting circuits, inspection and testing of installations, and the installation of bells and secondary cells. All the explanations have clear illustrations to guide you through the correct procedures. You can check your knowledge with the multi-choice questions at the end of each chapter, and the information sheets, packed with useful tips, provide a quick summary of the essential facts.

R. D. Puckering

Acknowledgements

The Institute of Electrical Engineers
J. A. Crabtree & Co Ltd
M. K. Electric Ltd
Pyrotenax Ltd
Central Generating Board
Rawlplug Ltd
British Insulated Callander Cables Ltd
Wylex (Scholes)
Martindale
Chloride Gent

Chapter 1
The Generation and Transmission of Electricity

1.1 The generation of electricity

The siting of power stations

The electricity supply for the vast majority of installations in Great Britain comes in the first instance from power stations run by the Central Electricity Generating Board (CEGB). Good use is made of the natural resources to be found in this country, and the power stations are usually sited close to these resources. A lot of attention is paid to the aesthetic effect of these installations, especially on sites of great natural beauty, and where it is important, the CEGB make good use of landscaping, tree planting and local stone to blend these into the countryside.

Coal burning stations

Most of the power stations are still coal-fired for the purpose of raising steam to drive the turbo-generators which produce the electricity (see Fig. 1.1). Well over 60 million tonnes of coal are used each year, so these power stations tend to be situated near the coal fields of north-east England, Yorkshire, Derbyshire, Wales and Kent in order to reduce the cost of transportation.

These stations produce large amounts of ash as a waste product, some of which is sold for use in road building or the manufacture of building blocks. Some of it is piped as a slurry of ash and water into settling lagoons, which are often old sand or gravel pits. After draining the water off, it is either left as an infill and the land returned to agricultural use, or it can be removed and used for other purposes.

Pollution is a problem, and the CEGB, who are one of the leading authorities on this, spend millions of pounds on the development, installation and operation of equipment to prevent dust, grit and sulphur from reaching the atmosphere.

Oil burning stations

There are not as many oil-fired power stations as there are coal-fired. Despite this fact, well over 13 million tonnes of fuel oil is burned every year. In order to reduce the expense of transporting the oil great distances, these stations are mainly constructed beside the oil refineries of south-west Wales,

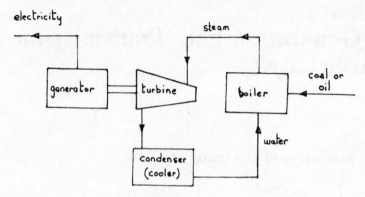

Fig. 1.1 The thermal process of generation.

southern and south-east England. Others are near to the deep water ports, so that oil can be shipped in by tankers when it is in cheap and plentiful supply. With the discovery of North Sea oil, some of the coal-fired plants were converted to oil and the fuel piped in directly from the terminals. Oil-fired power stations are similar in many respects to the coal-fired ones, although there is no coal handling or pulverising plant.

Nuclear power stations

There are very few nuclear power stations in Great Britain, compared to such countries as France which generates most of her electrical energy this way. The amount of fuel used in this type of power station is very small, because in an advanced reactor, as much electricity can be made out of 1 kg of enriched uranium as from 50 tonnes of coal. The siting of these power stations is not easy, however, as great resistance to them is being put forward on environmental and ecological grounds. The used fuel, which is radioactive, is loaded into special thick steel flasks and taken by rail to British Nuclear Fuels Ltd for reprocessing.

Hydroelectric schemes

The three types of power station described above use either fossil fuels or nuclear fuel to heat water, and produce steam to drive the turbines. This is called the *thermal process*. It is not the only way of providing the prime mover (means of turning) to drive the generators. In areas where there is a good continuous flow of water, such as parts of Scotland and Wales, the natural force of the water can be used to drive the turbines. Environmentalists have mixed feelings about this type of power station. On the one hand, they are free from the pollution problems of the other types of station while, on the other hand, they flood large tracts of land to provide the reservoirs which are a requirement for this type of power generation. Once the initial cost of building the reservoirs, dams, penstock (pipelines) and generating plant is over, the running of these types of power station is relatively cheap. They do, however, depend on the weather to a certain extent to keep up a constant supply of water (see Fig. 1.2).

Pumped storage schemes

A hydroelectric scheme, which overcomes to some extent the problem of dependency on the weather, is the pumped storage scheme. In simple terms, this consists of a hydroelectric power station situated between an upper re-servoir and a lower one. The water is allowed to flow from the upper reservoir through the turbines and out into the lower reservoir, thus generating the electricity. When the water in the upper reservoir reaches a certain level, pumps using off-peak electricity take the water from the lower reservoir back up to the higher level. The level of the water is kept topped up by the natural rain-fall in the area. However, suitable sites are very difficult to find and are usually in places of great natural beauty. This apart, these power stations have much to offer; they are pollution-free, economical to run, and have the added advantage of being able to be brought on line at short notice. This is a particularly useful asset for the CEGB, who bring these power stations into use when faced with sudden high demands for energy, such as an unexpected cold spell, for example.

Alternative means of generation

The CEGB are constantly looking at alternative ways of generating electricity, and much pressure has been put on them recently by environmentalists to

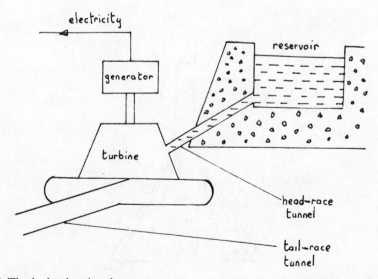

Fig. 1.2 The hydroelectric scheme.

make use of what they see as pollution-free methods. It might be a good idea to look at some of these schemes and see just what they would entail.

Wind power   For this type of electrical generation, wind is required and lots of it. It has to be strong and fairly constant. In the British Isles, the Orkneys and Shetland Isles meet these requirements, and wind-driven generators are used to good effect in small communities there (see Fig. 1.3). To generate electricity on the scale required to equal the output of even a small, conventional type of power station, it is estimated that well over 100 square km of these would be required.

Wave power   Experiments are being carried out and schemes are being evaluated in the use of wave power for the generation of electricity. If the principle of converting the up-and-down motion of the waves into a reciprocating motion required to turn the generators is practical and economical, then Britain as an island would be indeed fortunate, as we are surrounded by the sea. At the time of writing, however, no positive schemes have emerged for the use of wave power.

Solar power   Solar panels, mounted on the roofs of houses, can prove very cost-effective when it comes to the heating of water, and in hot regions such as the Mediterranean, North Africa and the southern most states of the United States of America, all the household requirements for heating and hot water can be obtained this way. Experiments are still going on, and scientists at Harwell Research Unit carrying out experiments found that an average of

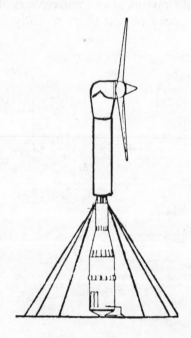

Fig. 1.3 Wind generator.

0.2 kW of heat can be obtained per square metre an hour over most of Britain. At the moment, it does seem impracticable on a large scale, as some six million square metres of converting surface would be required to produce 2000 mW of electricity.

Tidal barrages Of all the alternative schemes being evaluated at the moment, this seems to be the most viable. The principle behind the operation of this type of generating plant is to make use of the difference in water levels between high tide and low tide. Once again, Britain is fortunate in this respect as more than half the potentially suitable sites in Europe are situated here. The idea is to build a barrage across an estuary or bay, and allow sea water at high tide to flow in behind the barrier. When high tide is reached, gates are closed trapping the water behind the barrage. The water is allowed to flow out again at low tide, but first it must pass over the turbines of a generating station, thus producing electricity. This is a pollution-free method, but environmentalists will have to weigh this against the building of these stations at such beauty spots as the Bristol Channel and Morecambe Bay, two of the spots potentially suitable for this type of enterprise.

1.2 The transmission of electricity

Early developments in electrical distribution

In 1925, there were between 400 and 500 power stations in Great Britain. They were sited in or near the towns they were to serve and were, with few exceptions, independent of neighbouring power stations. Their size depended to some extent on the area they had to serve, but would on average be of around 5000 kW. There was no standardisation of voltage or frequency, in fact many were of the direct current (DC) type and not the alternating current (AC) that is used today. This independent policy not only created confusion when people moved equipment from one part of the country to the other, but it hindered technical development too. Clearly something had to be done about the situation, and in 1926 an Act of Parliament was passed forming what was then known as the Central Electricity Board. The Board had the task of interconnecting the largest and most efficient power stations with a system of high voltage transmission lines operating at 132 000 V 50 Hz. This became known as the *grid system*.

The main purpose of the grid system was to operate the interconnected stations, so that the greatest number of units of electricity were generated by the then most efficient plant available. There were a number of other important advantages as follows:

- Standardisation of frequency and voltage;
- Less reserve plant required;
- Security of supplies;
- Energy transfer on a country-wide basis;
- Power stations sited near source of fuel;
- No need for stations to be in town centres.

As the demand for electricity increased, so did the size of the electricity supply industry to cope with it. In 1947, the whole of the industry was nationalised and in 1957, the name of the Central Electricity Board was changed to The Central Electricity Generating Board (CEGB). The distances that the electricity was being carried had increased too and to achieve greater efficiency, the transmission voltages had to go higher and higher until we have what is known today as the *super grid*.

The national grid

The large modern power stations generate electricity at something like 25 000 V, but, as we have seen, for efficient transmission over long distances, the voltage is increased. The reason for this is that for a given load the current is reduced with increased voltage; thus the cross-sectional area (csa) of the conductors can be reduced making a saving on cable costs. Energy losses are also reduced and transmission efficiency is improved, but this is offset to some extent by the need for higher towers (pylons) and better insulators. The voltages required to do this are 132 000, 275 000 and 400 000 V, and these are achieved by the use of *step-up* transformers. The electricity is transmitted at these high voltages to bulk supply points, where it is reduced by use of *step-down* transformers for distribution by the various Area Boards, at 33 000 V for heavy industry, 11 000 V for light industry and 415/240 V for commercial premises, farms and homes (see Information Sheet No. 1A).

1.3 The effects of the introduction of electricity

It would be hard to imagine the modern world as we know it today without the use of electricity; almost every facet of our lives is touched by this form of energy. Some of the ways it affects us are shown below:

In the home   It is used for lighting, heating and cooking, as well as operating such devices as vacuum cleaners, electric irons, kettles, and many other appliances.

Health and welfare   Our hospitals use it to good effect for operating theatre lighting, X-ray machines, sterilising equipment and a host of other devices.

Security   Fire alarm systems, intruder alarms and warning systems of various sorts are all operated by electricity for our safety and security.

Leisure pursuits   Imagine football and greyhound stadiums without floodlighting, or track events without electronic timing and the photo-finish. These could not be done so effectively or as accurately without the use of electricity.

Entertainment   The home especially has been revolutionised by the use of such devices as television, video recorders, hi-fi equipment, etc. Theatres,

Information Sheet No. 1A Transmission and distribution of electricity.

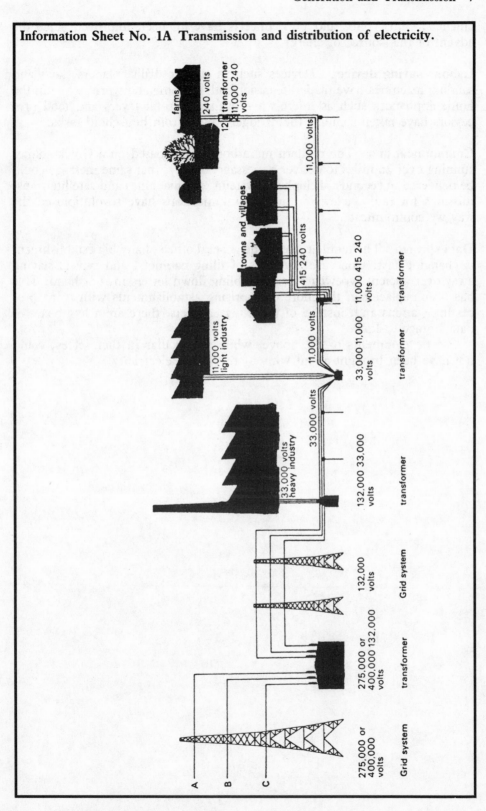

cinemas, clubs, pubs and pop concerts have all been improved since the advent of this source of energy.

Labour saving devices   Devices such as electric drills, planers, saws and sanding machines have made life easier both at home and work, while in the home appliances such as micro-wave ovens, deep-fat fryers and food processors have taken some of the drudgery away from household tasks.

Communications   The modern marathon race is based on a Greek soldier running over 26 miles to deliver a message. Today, that same message could be delivered in seconds. Telephone systems, fax machines and satellite transmissions for radio, television and communications have revolutionised the way we communicate.

Data storage   The familiar site of the general office of any big establishment is changing fast. Gone are the rows of filing cabinets, and typists slaving away over ancient typewriters or scribbling down letters in shorthand. This has been replaced in the more enterprising establishments with word processing stations and, instead of the filing cabinets, there are a few boxes of data storage disks.

The developments of the above, while spectacular in themselves, could not have been brought about without the use of electricity.

Test 1

Choose which of the four answers is the correct one.

(1) Power stations that burn fossil fuels use:

(a) Enriched uranium;
(b) The thermal process;
(c) Hydroelectricity;
(d) Pumped storage.

(2) The purpose of the *national grid system* is:

(a) To utilise available energy efficiently;
(b) To distribute low voltage supplies;
(c) To reach outlying farms;
(d) To save digging up the road.

(3) High voltages are used to transmit electricity because:

(a) They deter people from touching the conductors;
(b) Factories need the high voltages to work their machines;
(c) For a given load, the current is reduced with high voltages;
(d) Power stations generate electricity at these high voltages.

(4) The main advantage of a *pumped storage scheme* is:

(a) It uses up large amounts of rain water;
(b) It uses *off-peak* electricity;
(c) It provides fishing areas for anglers;
(d) It can *come on line* quickly.

(5) The *prime mover* for hydroelectric schemes is:

(a) Water;
(b) Steam;
(c) Gas;
(d) Nuclear fission.

Chapter 2
The Maintenance of Health and Safety at Work

2.1 Health and safety at work

Health and Safety at Work etc. Act 1974

Health and safety legislation originates from as far back as 1802, and since then has been added to by many new acts and regulations. Much of this legislation, however, is being brought together under the Health and Safety at Work etc. Act 1974. The Act seeks to replace the complex system of laws, rules and regulations with a less complicated arrangement based on Approved Codes of Practice.

The 1974 Act is designed to protect the health and safety of people at work, and places duties on employer and employee alike. It comes under the authority of the Health and Safety Commission, and the body responsible for putting the decisions of the Commission into practice is the Health and Safety Executive. Any person in breach of the provisions of the Act can, at the will of a visiting Inspector, be prosecuted, which, if successful, can result in a heavy fine or imprisonment. In fact, it is more usual for the Inspector to issue a prohibition notice stopping the activity or, if it is less serious, an improvement notice to remedy the fault in a given period of time. Prosecution under these circumstances would only follow if the notices were not complied with.

In practice, much of the safety aspects of doing particular jobs of work are taught as and when the operation is being carried out. For example, if you were drilling a metal bracket, you would be instructed that it would be advisable to wear safety goggles to prevent pieces of metal inadvertently entering the eye. These, and other safety aspects of particular jobs of work, will be discussed in future chapters; however, it might be a good idea to look at the more general implications of the 1974 Act as it affects people working in the electrical contracting industry.

2.2 The employer's responsibility

Under the Act, the employer is responsible as far as is practicable for the health, safety and welfare of all their employees at work. This applies particularly to the following:

Safe place of work

Employers are required to see that, as far as is practical, the place of work is safe for you to carry out your job. On building sites, the weather plays a big part in safety aspects, for example, slippery surfaces caused by ice, snow or water can present a hazard, especially at the entrances to sites and on concrete staircases open to the weather. This makes access to the place of work difficult and, therefore, in the interests of safety, these should be kept clear and treated with sand or salt to ensure safe passage for the employees. No one should be required to leap open trenches or climb mounds of loose earth, in order to get to their place of work. Designated safe routes should be provided for both vehicles and pedestrians, with plastic tapes or barriers indicating the extent of any danger areas. Staircases to upper floors should have temporary handrails provided and any openings in floors or edges to buildings should have safety barriers erected around them. Where people are working at different levels, there is always the chance that tools or building materials can fall to the lower floors. In situations such as this, toe boards should be provided on building edges and scaffolding (see Information Sheet No. 2A). In existing buildings, entrances and exits should be clearly identified and kept clear of obstructions. Gangways should be marked by yellow lines, and warning notices posted if used by vehicular traffic. The building should be adequately lit by artificial or natural light, and comply with local and national regulations regarding the building's structure, fire precautions, emergency lighting and other building services such as gas, electricity, telephones, etc.

Provision of safe plant and equipment

It is the employer's duty under the 1974 Act to see that all plant and equipment, whether it be fixed equipment in a workshop or portable equipment on site, is safe to use and in good working order. Regular checks should be carried out to see that equipment and plant complies with the appropriate standards with respect to the health and safety of employees (for electrical equipment see Chapter 3). We have seen that it is the employer's responsibility to provide safe access to the place of work and if this involves the use of access equipment (ladders, etc.) then these too should be maintained in a sound and servicable condition (see Information Sheet No. 2B). It is the employee's duty to check the ladders, etc., before use, and to use them in the recommended way (see Information Sheets Nos 2C and 2D). Many items of equipment are now fitted with safety features such as fences on circular saws, perspex screens on grindstones, safety guards on rotating machinery and dust extraction equipment on cutting and forming machines. These should not be removed under any circumstances; they are fitted for your safety, and removal could make them dangerous for you or for people following after you. It is for this reason that employers are obliged under the terms of the Act to give their employees full instructions for the use of potentially dangerous equipment, and, where necessary, post working notices on the operation of systems and machinery. It is essential that these safety devices are regularly checked and are in place (see section 2(1) and 2(2) of the Act).

Information Sheet No. 2A Scaffolding.

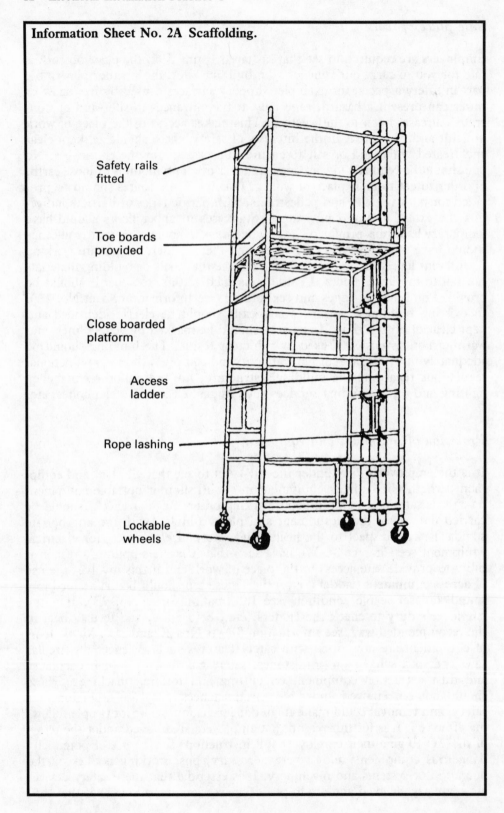

Safety rails
fitted

Toe boards
provided

Close boarded
platform

Access
ladder

Rope lashing

Lockable
wheels

Information Sheet No. 2B Ladder safety checks.

Check ladders for the following defects:

No cracks on styles

No splits in rungs

No dirt on rungs

No temporary repairs

No wood rot

No damaged tie-rods

No warping

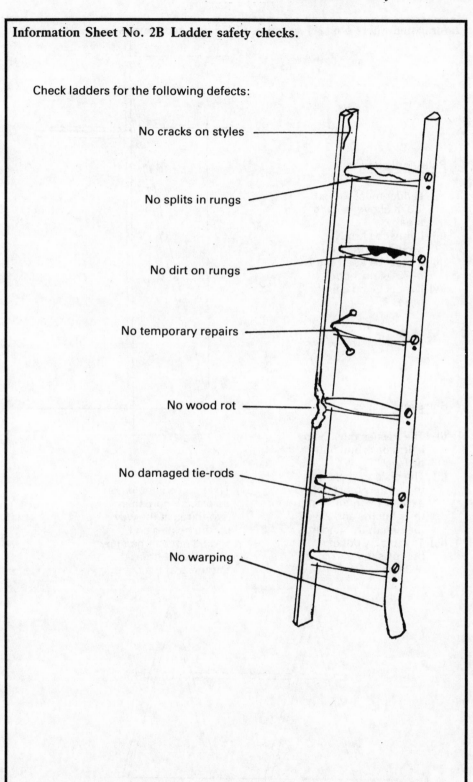

Information Sheet No. 2C Erection of ladders and trestles.

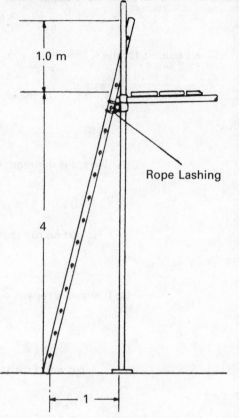

1.0 m

Rope Lashing

4

1

Rules for Ladders

(i) Ladder must extend 1.0 m above landing area

(ii) It must be firmly secured at the top

(iii) It must be at an angle of 75° (4 up 1 out)

(iv) It must be on a firm base.

Rules for Trestles

(i) The trestles must be on a firm base and both be level

(ii) The distance between the trestles must not exceed 1.3 m for 40 mm thick boards and 2.5 m for 50 mm thick boards

(iii) The total width of boards should exceed 450 mm

(iv) The boards should not be placed more than two-thirds of the way up the trestles and should not overhang by more than 4 times the thickness of the boards.

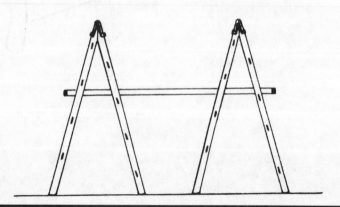

Information Sheet No. 2D Handling ladders.

1. With the ladder in the
   upright position rest
   it on the shoulder. If
   you are right-handed
   reach down with your
   right hand one rung
   lower than you would
   normally reach when
   standing erect. Lift by
   straightening the knees.
   Get your balance
   correct before
   moving off.

2. When moving ladders which are
   heavy or for long distances, then
   two people must be used as
   shown in the sketch.

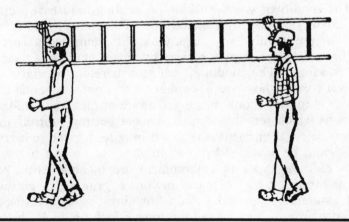

Safe systems of work

Some of the jobs which people in the electrical contracting industry undertake are either potentially dangerous or are carried out in potentially dangerous situations. It is for that reason that employers have to ensure that procedures and systems of work are designed to safeguard the health and safety of those putting them into practice. Potentially dangerous situations might be as follows:

- Close to high voltage equipment;
- Working in deep excavations;
- Petrochemical installations;
- Processes giving off toxic fumes;
- Nuclear plants.

Access to these areas is prohibited and before entry can be obtained a *permit to work* must be obtained. An example of such a permit is shown in Fig. 2.1. This is a working procedure, whereby people wishing to enter restricted areas must obtain permission to do so from an authorised person. This ensures the following safeguards are observed:

(1) The area is safe for you to enter;
(2) Other people are aware that you are in there;
(3) The task you are carrying out is permissible;
(4) It will be known when you have left the area.

Working systems such as this are for your safety and should under no circumstances be abused.

A number of safety systems installed for your protection, such as emergency stop buttons, residual current devices, fire alarm systems, etc., are not in constant use and therefore should be regularly tested at appropriate intervals to ensure that they are still operating correctly.

The workplace environment

This will depend to a large extent on the sort of contract upon which you are working. The conditions when working on existing industrial premises will to a large extent be fairly well established. The company or organisation responsible for the building will already have implemented a safety policy, which will be subjected to regular reviews by representatives of their management and workforce. The conditions will not therefore be under your employer's direct control, however, if certain adverse environmental conditions do exist, your employer should make you aware of these, and inform you of the precautions which you should take to avoid putting yourself and others at risk. If any safety equipment is required in order for you to carry out the work, this should be provided by your employer at no cost to yourself.

Examples of these types of environment are manufacturing processes, which use or produce toxic chemicals or fumes; grinding or cutting operations which produce fine particles of dust or fibres; manufacturing methods employing corrosive substances, and machines which produce a high pitched

DEPARTMENT OF THE CHIEF ELECTRICAL ENGINEER
PERMIT
(PERMIT TO WORK·
ON HIGH VOLTAGE ELECTRICAL APPARATUS OTHER THAN HIGH VOLTAGE CABLES)

Serial numbers of associated Isolation Certificates ....

ISSUE

To: Name ....

Grade ....   Depot ....

I have read and understand Parts 1 & 2 of High Voltage Safety Rules and I hereby declare that it is safe to work on the following high voltage apparatus :—

That apparatus is dead and isolated from all live conductors at the following point(s):

Associated voltage and/or control transformers have also been isolated

The apparatus is efficiently connected to earth at the following point(s):

1 ....
2 ....
3 ....
4 ....
5 ....
6 ....

Caution notices are posted at ....

Danger notices are posted at ....

Safety barriers are erected at ....
ALL OTHER PARTS ARE DANGEROUS

The following is the work to be carried out on the apparatus:—

Issued with the consent of ....

SHIFT SUPPLY ENGINEER

SIGNED...
being an Authorised person possessing
authority to issue a Permit for the work specified above

Time ....hours .... 19...... Location ....

311/69 (100/100 5/73 406) 2 part set

Fig. 2.1 Permit to work.

or excessively loud sound. Many of these processes can be dangerous to the eyes, lungs, skin or ears, and any goggles, masks, ear muffs, respirators or protective clothing, provided for your use, should be worn at all times whilst working in such areas. The employees should make it their business to find out what working procedures or rules apply when working in these environments, as often *permits to work* are required before you can enter certain areas. Other potentially hazardous conditions are processes using inflammable materials; in this situation, all notices regarding fire prevention should be observed and the operatives should make themselves familiar with the recommended fire-drill. Further details on fire prevention can be found in Chapter 3.

On building sites where you are carrying out new work, the rules and procedures for safety may not be so well laid down as the above, although all the safety rules still apply. Adverse weather plays a big part in the sort of environmental conditions that exist, and although there is little an employer can do about this, wellington boots and water-proof clothing should be provided for employees spending large amounts of time outside. Not only does this mean that operatives are kept dry and warm, but it also means that the job can proceed even if the weather is a little inclement. Protective clothing of this nature is essential for people laying underground cables, erecting overhead lines and those installing outdoor equipment. Where people are working at different levels, there is always the chance that tools or building materials can fall to the lower floors; in these situations safety hats should be provided by the employer and worn by the operatives (see Fig. 2.2). Facilities on the bigger sites are run under what is known as *shared welfare schemes*; that is to say that all the employers of the various trades working on the site, have contributed, as part of the terms of the contract, to the supplying of certain welfare provisions. These often take the form of portable toilets, washrooms, canteens, first-aid facilities and drying rooms for wet outdoor clothes. Ask your employer what provisions have been made on the site you are working on.

The handling, transportation and storage of equipment

The handling of equipment starts with the basic act of lifting a piece of equipment up and placing it in another position, for example, onto a bench

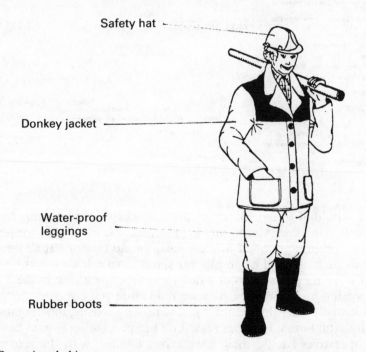

Safety hat

Donkey jacket

Water-proof leggings

Rubber boots

Fig. 2.2 Protective clothing.

Information Sheet No. 2E Lifting objects.

1. Feet should be about 0.5 m apart, one foot slightly forward.
2. Knees should be bent slightly.
3. Back must be straight.
4. Arms must be kept close to the body.
5. Head should be erect with the chin tucked in.

6. Take a firm grip of the object.
7. Lift by straightening the legs, not by pulling with the arms.
8. Keep the object close to the body and look in a forward direction.
9. Place the object on a firm base before letting it go.

10. Any load over 20 kg will require some assistance.
11. Lift as before with one person giving the instructions.

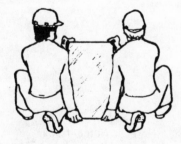

or into the back of a van. It sounds so simple, yet the resulting back strain, due to incorrect posture when lifting or handling goods or equipment, is one of the major reasons for lost working days in industry. Information Sheet No. 2E shows the correct method of manually lifting loads. Any load over 20 kg in weight would normally need some form of assistance, and Information Sheet No. 2E shows methods of moving equipment by *team lifting*. The moving of really heavy equipment, such as large oil filled transformers or emergency generating equipment, is best left to experts trained in the moving of heavy plant. Not only are they well practised in the techniques of lifting and moving, but they will do it more quickly, more safely and without damage to the equipment. Advice should be sought when moving potentially dangerous substances, as incorrect procedures can result in serious spillage or even explosions. There are occasions, however, when the operative is required to use lifting gear, for example, off-loading equipment that has been delivered to site. This often takes the form of simple block and tackle, which is either manually operated or is powered by an electric motor (see Fig. 2.3). The use of this type of equipment is not beyond the scope of the average electrician, but it must be stressed once again that full instructions as to its proper use should have been received prior to attempting a lifting operation.

The moving of goods and equipment over long distances requires the use of some form of wheeled transportation. This, in its elementary form, could be a *sack barrow* or hand truck; these are the simple two-wheeled devices once much used by British Rail porters. Great care must be taken that these are not overloaded, and that you have a clear view of where you are going. Another method is to use a flat trailer. A great deal of equipment can be

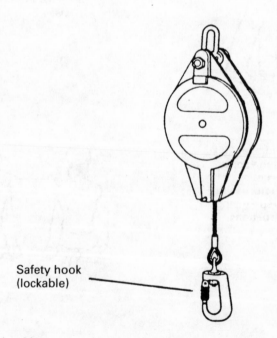

Safety hook
(lockable)

Fig. 2.3 Block and tackle.

moved in this way, but care must be taken to see that it is securely fastened down and, if the equipment is circular in shape, to see that it is chocked so that it cannot roll (see Fig. 2.4). Some of these flat trailers have only three wheels, and care should be taken when turning corners with this design, as they can topple over on tight bends. Fork-lift trucks are, without doubt, a most versatile piece of equipment, not only for off-loading equipment, but for moving equipment too. Many of the goods sent to site are now dispatched on pallets; that is to say special timber frames designed so that the fork-lift truck can engage and disengage its forks without disturbing the load. This has improved the distribution of goods to such an extent that few premises or sites are without them. There are many restrictions on the use of fork-lift trucks regarding types of loads, heights they can be lifted, etc., and under no circumstances should petrol or diesel operated trucks be used inside buildings. Before attempting to make use of a fork-lift truck, make sure you are fully instructed in its use and that you are covered by insurance.

Storage of equipment on sites can be reduced to a minimum by having materials scheduled for delivery just prior to the time that they are wanted. Delays and alterations do occur and some storage facilities will have to be provided for this and the usual day-to-day items. Storage raises several important points which should be observed; the main ones are as follows:

- Expensive equipment and that on long delivery should be placed under lock and key;
- Equipment which is easily damaged should be protected from breakage by packaging, etc.;
- Certain items, such as galvanised cable tray, conduit and trunking, can be placed in outside compounds;
- Equipment which can be damaged by the weather should be placed under cover;

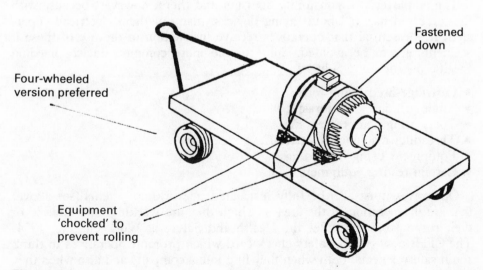

Fig. 2.4 Flat trailer.

- Goods should not be placed in designated gangways or walkways, as this can cause obstruction in the case of an emergency;
- Entrances and exits should be kept clear of goods and equipment for the same reason;
- Dangerous substances should be placed in designated compounds and be clearly marked;
- Inflammable substances should likewise be placed in approved compounds and be clearly marked;
- Locked storage facilities should be provided for employees, tools and equipment.

The training and instruction of employees

The training and instruction of the operatives in the electrical contracting industry is the responsibility of the employers in the industry. Not only are they responsible for training and instruction in necessary skills of the trade, but they are also responsible for seeing that operatives receive instruction on all aspects of safety, as outlined in the 1974 Act. Many of the employers in the electrical contracting industry have their apprentices trained under the Joint Industry Board (JIB)/Construction Industry Training Board (CITB) training scheme. Under this scheme, junior apprentices will be expected to take the City and Guilds 236 Craft Certificate (Part 1) in Electrical Installation and also pass a practical test called Achievement Measurement 1 (AM1). If successful, the apprentice will be graded Senior Apprentice (Stage 1). Following this, the City and Guilds 236 Craft Certificate (Part 2) in Electrical Installation is taken and, if successful, the apprentice is graded Senior Apprentice (Stage 2). When a further degree of skill and knowledge has been achieved, the apprentice will take a further practical test called the Achievement Measurement 2 (AM2). Success in this will complete the training and lead to eligibility for grading to Electrician.

The employer's responsibility does not end there, however, because with the increased use of labour-saving devices, many of them electrically operated, it is essential that operatives receive instruction in the use of these if accidents are to be avoided. Some of the more common devices needing specific instruction would be:

- Cartridge-fired fixing tools;
- Angle grinders and abrasive wheels;
- Tools using compressed air;
- Threading machines (electrical);
- Equipment using bottled gas;
- Certain testing equipment.

Operatives must also be fully instructed in working systems (see above) that are in operation in the area in which they are working, and advised of their responsibilities under the Health and Safety at Work etc. Act 1974. The CITB now issue a safety check card which prompts operatives to think about safety aspects, both when they first join a company and also when they go out on site.

Safety policy

Safety policy in a small company may well be by word of mouth; bigger companies will find it almost impossible to see every one of their employees regularly. It is under these circumstances that the recommendations of the Safety Representative, and Safety Committee Regulations 1977, might prove to be useful. Safety policy, subject to regular review jointly by employers' and employees' representatives, is by far the best and easiest way of producing a common policy acceptable to all concerned. The safety policy should concern itself with all aspects of safety applicable to the type of work the company carries out, and should include things like the reporting of accidents, the keeping of accident registers (Notification of Accidents and General Occurrences Regulations 1980) and instruction and training in safety matters.

Public liability

If work involving major alterations or additions to domestic or commercial premises takes place in a vacated building or an area that has been sealed off from the general public, then the environmental conditions are much like those on the building site above. Electrical contractors, however, are often asked to carry out work in buildings where people are still in residence or which are open to the general public. The 1974 Act makes the employer responsible for seeing that any work being carried out is done so in such a way as not to endanger other persons who may not be in their employ, and this includes residents and customers as well as other tradespeople. Companies have by law to take out public liability insurance if their work can endanger people other than their own employees (employees are covered separately). Employers should make it quite clear to their employees how they should conduct the work under these circumstances, and they should supply any special requirements such as dust sheets, temporary lighting, etc., to protect the property and ensure the health, safety and welfare of all concerned.

2.3 Employees' responsibility

Employees too have responsibilities under the Act and, in general, these are as follows:

Responsibility to themselves and others

Employers can provide you with safety equipment and instruct you in the use of it. They can provide you with equipment to help you do your job more easily and efficiently, and see that this is kept in good condition, but they cannot cater for what is often called 'human error'. Most accidents don't just happen; they are caused by people's actions, or failure to take the appropriate action when faced with potentially dangerous situations. The person who knowingly uses a damaged piece of equipment is guilty of negligence, but so is the person who sees the damage and does not report it. You are responsible under the terms of the 1974 Act to see that your actions not only leave you free from hazard, but that they leave other people around you free from hazard too. We have seen how dangerous ice and snow can make surfaces. These dangers are not only attributable to weather, however; substances such as oil, grease, cutting compounds, paints and solvents spilled on the floor and not dealt with immediately can cause hazards. Even things like food, leaves from nearby trees and the off-cuts of conduit and pipe are dangerous if left underfoot. Clearly employees have some responsibility both to themselves and others to keep the workplace hazard free.

Follow the safety procedures

Employees must co-operate with their employers to carry out the duties of the Act, i.e., they must follow the safety codes laid down and make full use of any safety equipment provided. For example, any safety procedures such as the permit to work must not be abused by trying to take short cuts with paper work, etc. To do so would mean that the authorised person would have no way of knowing if you were in the area, and may take action that would place you in danger. When you are supplied with safety equipment, it might feel uncomfortable and you may not always see the need for it. A safety helmet, for example, feels very awkward at first, but if you persevere you will soon get used to it. By taking the helmet off and leaving it in the canteen or elsewhere, you are leaving yourself open to injury from falling objects, and if you were to be seriously injured it is unlikely that you would receive any sort of compensation if the employer could prove that you had been issued with a safety helmet.

Interference with articles or substances

Under the Act, no person may intentionally misuse or recklessly interfere with any article or substance, so as to put at risk the health and safety of themselves or others. Do not, for example, remove ladders from one part of the site to another without first checking that they are not in use. You may leave someone stranded up a scaffold, or, worse still, they may try to come down a ladder that is no longer there. The construction industry uses many different substances that are potentially dangerous. Do not get into the habit of opening any tins or containers just to see what is inside; they may contain substances dangerous to the skin, or give off fumes which can seriously affect the eyes or throat.

Misuse of equipment

Employees must not misuse or interfere in any way with items of equipment provided for their health, safety or welfare. We saw earlier that fences,

screens and guards are fitted to rotating machinery; these should not be removed under any circumstances, even if you feel that they are slowing the
operation down. These are fitted for your safety and removal could mean at
best that you were liable for prosecution under the terms of the Act, or at
worst serious injury to yourself or others for which there would be little, if
any, compensation.

Reasons for accidents

The construction industry has a worse record for accidents than any other
single industry. We have seen that many of these accidents are due to human
or environmental reasons; let's have a look at some of these:

Human This can be due to a number of reasons, such as carelessness, tired-
ness, improper behaviour (horseplay) and dress, the taking of drugs for health
reasons, drug abuse, the drinking of alcohol, poor eyesight, colour blindness,
lack of experience, poor supervision, and lack of proper instruction.

Environmental Taking the meaning of the word in its broadest sense,
hazards could result from inadequate ventilation, poor lighting, hostile environment, overcrowding, inclement weather, unsafe plant and equipment,
lack of safety equipment, or a dirty or untidy workplace.

Reducing the risk of accidents

The best way to reduce the risks of accidents is to try and remove the cause.
Providing adequate lighting at the workplace would reduce accidents caused
by people not being able to see things clearly, and also extend the working
day in winter time. Locking dangerous substances in approved compounds
so that people would not be tempted to interfere with them, causing danger
to themselves and others, would remove another potential hazard.

If a hazard cannot be removed totally, then it might be possible to replace
the risk with something less dangerous. For example, electric hand tools on
site should be designed to be used on 110 V AC (55 V to earth) and not
240 V AC, thus reducing the risk of severe electric shock (see Chapter 3).

Hazards that cannot be removed or reduced can be guarded against; guards
and fences can be put on machines, for example, or safety helmets or goggles
issued, or hair nets provided for long hair, and other protective clothing
supplied for your personal protection. Personal hygiene is important and
barrier creams should be available for the hands, as well as the usual toilet
and washing facilities.

It is necessary to develop a positive personal attitude towards safety in
people's minds if the safety record is to be improved, and one of the best
ways to achieve this is by safety instruction and education, and by a strong
publicity drive pointing out the dangers. It is said that safety is expensive,
but so too is the alternative, in lost time, damaged equipment, compensation
for injuries and the needless loss of life.

Test 2

Choose which of the four answers is the correct one.

(1) The Act of Parliament concerning health and safety at work is:

(a) The Health and Safety Act 1974;
(b) The Health and Safety etc. at Work Act 1974;
(c) The Health and Safety at Work etc. Act 1974;
(d) The Health and Safety at Work Act 1974.

(2) The above Act of Parliament is for the guidance of:

(a) Employees only;
(b) Members of the public only;
(c) Employers only;
(d) Employers and employees.

(3) An example of access equipment would be:

(a) A spare hacksaw;
(b) An extension ladder;
(c) A banker's card;
(d) Too much conduit.

(4) When lifting equipment the main muscles used should be the:

(a) Back muscles;
(b) Arm muscles;
(c) Muscles in the legs;
(d) Muscles in the hands.

(5) A safety precaution when using an electric drill would be to:

(a) Use a slow speed;
(b) Drill a little deeper than required;
(c) Stand on a pair of step-ladders;
(d) Wear protective goggles.

Chapter 3
The Need for Wiring Regulations

3.1 Electrical safety

The need for the IEE Wiring Regulations

As the use of electricity became more popular, it soon became clear that some unified form of regulations, concerning its safe installation into buildings, would be necessary if serious accidents were to be avoided. It was for this reason that the first edition of the *Rules and Regulations for the Prevention of Fire Risks Arising from Electric Lighting* was published in 1882. The early Regulations set out to achieve the following:

(1) To safeguard the users of electrical energy from shock;
(2) To minimise fire risk;
(3) To ensure as far as possible the safe and satisfactory operation of apparatus.

The use of electricity as a form of energy has expanded at a tremendous rate since those days, and new editions of the Regulations have been brought out to keep pace with these developments. The latest edition published by the Institution of Electrical Engineers (IEE) is the 15th edition and is entitled *IEE Wiring Regulations – Regulations for Electrical Installations*. The full scope and objectives of these is described briefly in the Regulations in Chapters 11 and 12.

Statutory requirements

It is important to note that the IEE Wiring Regulations are not statutory; that is to say they are not law but only recommendations. However, several Acts of Parliament, notably the Electricity Supply Regulations 1988, and Electricity (Factories Act) Special Regulations 1908 and 1944, are in part commensurate with the IEE Wiring Regulations, and as these Acts are mandatory or established in law, it would be very difficult indeed to have an electrical installation connected to the public supply if it did not in fact comply with the IEE Wiring Regulations. No matter how complicated electrical installations have become, and how much the regulations have changed to accommodate them, the three basic objectives listed above are still as relevant today as they were then, and therefore it would be useful to look at them more closely.

3.2 Electric shock

How the human body can become part of an electric circuit.

The *Collins English Dictionary* defines electric shock as follows:

'The physiological reaction characterised by pain and muscular spasm to the passage of an electric current through the body. It can affect the respiratory system and heart rhythm'.

How does this condition come about? It can come about in two ways:

(1) If we connect the two leads of an approved test lamp across the phase and neutral connections of a circuit as shown in Fig. 3.1, and the circuit is switched on, the current will flow through the lamp and the lamp's filament will glow. This is because the lamp has completed a circuit between phase and neutral. Now if a person places themselves across the phase and neutral connections of a circuit, as shown on Information Sheet No. 3A, they too will have completed a circuit and current will attempt to flow through them as shown, and they will receive an electric shock.

(2) Most people will appreciate that an electric shock can also be received by the touching of a current-carrying conductor or a live part of electrical equipment. How then does this shock come about? We have seen from the first example that for current to flow, a circuit of some kind must be completed. In the second example, however, we are only touching the current-carrying conductor and not the neutral conductor as well; how then is the circuit completed? The circuit is completed, as shown on Information Sheet No. 3A, by the current passing once again through the body of the person, but this time it travels from phase to earth as shown. It will be seen that the current passes through the earth and returns to the star point of the supply authorities' transformer, which is in effect neutral, and so completes the circuit.

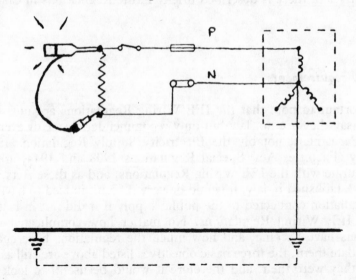

Fig. 3.1 Test lamp across the circuit.

Information Sheet No. 3A Electric shock. (i) Between poles;
(ii) Phase to earth.

(i)

(ii)

Action to be taken in the event of an electric shock

If a friend or colleague receives an electric shock and is still in contact with the source of supply you must act speedily to:

- Find the isolator for that circuit quickly, and turn off the supply; or
- Break the person's contact with the supply by the use of some insulating material such as a coat or a broom handle; and
- Take care not to come into direct contact with the person while they are touching the supply or you too will get a shock; and
- Lower the casualty to the floor taking care not to damage the head.

If the casualty is conscious, make him comfortable and give him reassurance. If you are in doubt about his condition, then get in touch with a doctor, and report the accident to the appropriate personnel.

Should the casualty be unconscious but breathing, loosen the clothing around his neck and waist and place the casualty in the recovery position (see Fig. 3.2). Keep a constant check on his breathing and pulse; improvise a suitable method to keep him warm and arrange for medical help if necessary.

When a casualty is found unconscious, but **not** breathing, then **take immediate action** and apply emergency resuscitation. There are two resuscitation techniques that you should be aware of:

(1) Mouth-to-mouth or mouth-to-nose;
(2) Holger–Neilson method.

Mouth-to-mouth resuscitation is by far the most commonly used form of resuscitation and is most effective in the event of electric shock. However, if the face has sustained injury, it may be more practical to use the Holger–Neilson method; both methods are shown on Information Sheets Nos 3B and 3C.

Isolation of electrical supplies

If electric shock is to be avoided, then it is highly desirable that the installation or equipment that is being worked upon is isolated from the mains supply. The IEE Wiring Regulations ask that, except for certain cases mentioned in Chapter 46 of the Regulations, every circuit shall be provided with means of isolation from the live supply conductors. In addition to the normal means of isolation at the mains position, electrically operated plant and

Fig. 3.2 The recovery position.

Information Sheet No. 3B Mouth to mouth resuscitation.

1. Lay the casualty on his or her back and check the mouth for blockages. If possible raise the casualty's shoulders with padding of some sort.

2. Make sure the head is well back and the air-way is clear.

3. Pinch the casualty's nose. Take a deep breath and seal the lips around the open mouth of the casualty.

4. Blow gently and firmly into the mouth; the chest should rise slightly as the lungs fill with your air. Repeat until casualty shows signs of recovery.

Information Sheet No. 3C Holger−Neilson method of resuscitation.

1. Place the casualty face downwards with the head to one side; check that the mouth is clear. Kneel in front of the casualty as shown and place both hands flat in the upper part of the back. Rock forward applying pressure with the hands.

2. Rock backwards sliding the hands along and under the arm-pits. Grasp the upper arms as shown and lift. This will bring air into the lungs.

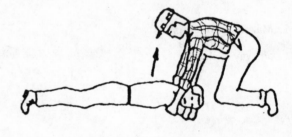

3. Lower the casualty gently down again.

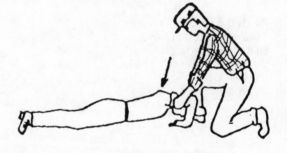

4. Repeat the operation over and over again until there is a sign of recovery. Lay the casualty in the 'recovery position'.

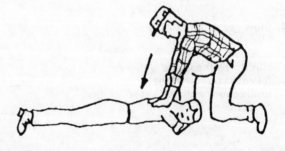

machinery should have a means of local isolation provided, readily identifiable and suitably placed, to give protection to persons carrying out mechanical or electrical maintenance.

In certain situations where it may be necessary to disconnect the supply rapidly to prevent or remove a hazard, a means of emergency switching should be provided. This usually takes the form of emergency stop buttons, which should be easily accessible and suitably identified. When these are operated they should not further increase the risk of hazard. All means of protection, switch fuses and isolators should be clearly marked. They should be capable of being locked in the off position so that they cannot be operated without the knowledge of persons working on that particular circuit. If the means of isolation is by fuses then these should be placed in the pocket or locked away, fuses should **never** be removed or replaced without first turning off the supply.

Before turning off a circuit, a check should be made to see that this will not cause problems for people in other parts of the building; computers, for example, can lose all their data if the supply is turned off unexpectedly. If the type of work you are doing exposes current carrying cables or equipment to touch, and other people could come into contact with them, then you should erect barriers to prevent this and notices should be placed in position indicating the dangers.

Testing that circuits are no longer live

It is the electrician's or instructed person's responsibility to ensure that when an isolator is operated that the circuit has been cut off from the supply. The test for this should be carried out by the use of an approved tester; that is to say one specifically designed for the job and not a lamp holder and flex, or even a neon tester which can be unreliable. Before putting the tester into use, it should be established that it is functioning correctly by testing it on a known source of supply. A typical approved tester is shown in Fig. 3.3. There are a number of different types of these available, and although they are not cheap they could save someone's life.

Reduced voltage tools and equipment

It is desirable (Health and Safety at Work etc. Act Rule 35) that where at all practical, tools and equipment used on site should be of the reduced voltage type. These are normally of the 110 V AC (55 V to earth) type and are readily available. Care should be taken of the equipment and the following safety rules should be observed:

- Do not use power tools on lighting circuits;
- Never carry power tools by their cables;
- Check power tools for damage regularly;
- Check cables for damage, especially where they enter equipment;
- Keep plugs and sockets clean and in good order;
- See that tools are fitted with the correct plug.

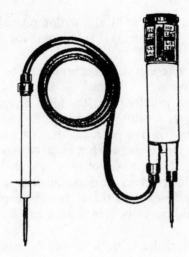

Fig. 3.3 Approved voltage tester.

The drawings in Information Sheet No. 3D show a typical 110 V transformer and plug, and a circuit diagram which shows the earthing arrangement.

The need for effective earthing

Many of the electric shocks that have been recorded in recent years could have been avoided if the electrical system concerned had been effectively earthed. We shall look at the subject of earthing in greater detail later; however, it will be worthwhile at this stage to examine earthing in the context of protection against electric shock.

If a fault was to occur between the phase conductor and the metalwork or exposed conductive parts of a piece of electrically operated equipment and a person was to touch it they would receive an electric shock. The intensity of the shock would depend on a number of factors, the health of the person receiving the shock, how well they were insulated from earth, i.e., if they were wearing wellingtons or standing on a wooden floor. Contact with water lowers the resistance of the body, so wet or damp situations such as bathrooms or showers are potentially dangerous. We have seen from the drawing on Information Sheet No. 3A that when the current passes through the person receiving a shock, it travels through the earth via the fault path back to the supply authorities' transformer. If we were to provide an alternative path for the fault current to pass through, then any fault current which flows in the metalwork would be conducted safely to earth. It is for this reason that the earthing of electrical installations by a system of protective conductors is carried out, and why it is so important that this is maintained in an effective condition.

Information Sheet No. 3D Reduced voltage supplies.

1. The BS 4343 plugs and sockets are used on construction sites for the distribution of electrical supplies. The 110 v plug and socket which is coloured yellow will be most familiar to the electrician.

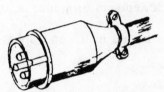

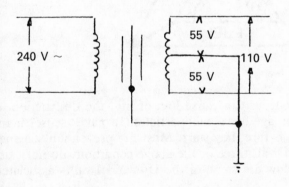

2. The 240 AC supply is transformed down to 110 V by the type of transformer shown.

3. This transformer ensures that only a maximum of 55 V to earth can be obtained if you come into contact with live parts.

3.3 Fire prevention

Conditions required for combustion

Before any fire can exist, three conditions have to be satisfied (see Fig. 3.4). If any one of the three is missing, then the fire cannot be sustained and will go out. The three conditions are as follows:

Fuel Any combustible material.

Heat Hot enough to ignite the material.

Oxygen Found in the atmosphere.

Fig. 3.4 The three conditions for fire.

When a fire does break out, it can cause loss of life, the destruction of buildings and the loss or damage of valuable articles. It makes sense therefore to try and prevent fires before they start. Most fire prevention schemes are based on making sure that all three of the above conditions do not exist at the same time. Listed below are some of the **Dos** and **Don'ts** associated with fire prevention:

Do	Don't
Do pay attention to no smoking signs;	Don't discard cigarette ends or matches carelessly;
Do store inflammable substances in approved stores or compounds;	Don't place inflammable materials near heat;
Do pay attention to warning signs about naked flames;	Don't put hot ashes or caustic materials in waste bins;
Do turn off heating appliances after use;	Don't leave bonfires unattended;
Do regularly check equipment using bottled gas for leaks;	Don't overload electrical circuits;

Do	Don't
Do ensure all electrical connections are secure;	Don't use equipment with damaged or worn flexes;
Do remember some substances give off vapours which can ignite;	Don't be careless when using blowlamps;
Do allow sufficient ventilation around equipment you install;	Don't fit equipment without backplates on inflammable surfaces.

Methods and equipment for extinguishing fires

The methods and equipment used to fight fires differs in accordance with the type of substance that is ignited. In Table 3.1 there are some of the more common substances that you would be likely to meet and the type of equipment you would use to put out the fire.

Table 3.1

Extinguisher	Colour	Type of fire	Remarks
Carbon dioxide	Black	Electrical, oil	Causes less damage to electrical equipment
Dry powder	Blue	Electrical, fires in petrol and diesel engines	
Water type	Red	Paper, wood, rags and over heated gas cylinders	Do not use on electrical or petrol fires
Foam or solvents etc.	Cream	Burning liquids: petrol, oil, paint	Will not spread the fire
Halogenated hydrocarbon, BCF	Green	Electrical, petrol and paint etc.	Do not use in confined spaces

Dangers associated with fire fighting

It is essential that the correct extinguisher is used when fighting fires, as the use of the wrong type can make matters worse. Water should not be used on petrol or oil fires, for example, as this tends to wash the liquid into new areas, so spreading the fire. Do not use water on electrical fires as water will conduct electricity and you could receive a shock.

Smaller fires can be put out by the use of sand or a fire-proof blanket, while in larger installations fires would be put out by the use of automatic systems, such as sprinklers, or the filling of a room with an inert gas. Whichever system is used, you should be aware of it and be able to act accordingly.

Remember that some materials, and in particular plastic materials, give off toxic fumes which can be harmful. Beware of smoke, and if the fire is too big leave the building quickly and calmly sounding the alarm as you go. If you have time, see that doors and windows are closed as this robs the fire of oxygen; however, leave them if this will endanger yourself. Most companies have fire drill procedures, and you should make yourself aware of these, and also the positions of alarm points, extinguishers and fire exits.

3.4 Fundamental requirements for safety

From the very early days of electricity there has been an essential requirement for electrical installations to be installed safely, as well as being suitable for the purpose that they were designed. The IEE Wiring Regulations give the basic requirements to achieve this in Chapter 13 of the Regulations and briefly they are as follows:

- Good workmanship and proper materials shall be used throughout the installation;
- The installation and equipment shall be installed in such a way as to be accessible for testing, inspection and maintenance;
- All equipment shall be suitable for the maximum power demand of the equipment when it is functioning in its intended manner;
- Electrical conductors shall be of sufficient size and current-carrying capacity for the purpose for which they are intended;
- Electrical conductors shall be insulated, protected and installed, so as to prevent danger as far as is practical;
- Joints and connections shall be properly constructed, regarding conductance, insulation, mechanical strength and protection;
- Where necessary, circuits will have suitably rated automatic protective devices for protection against overcurrent;
- Whenever the prospective earth fault current is insufficient to operate the above, a residual current device shall be fitted;
- Electrical equipment shall be earthed in such a manner that earth leakage currents will be discharged without danger;
- If metal parts of other services can be touched simultaneously with the above, then they should be earthed;
- No protective device shall be installed in an earthed neutral conductor, with the exception of a linked circuit breaker;
- Single pole switches shall be inserted in phase conductors, only with the exception of linked switches;
- Circuits supplying electrical equipment shall have effective means of isolation as necessary, to prevent or remove danger;
- Safe means of access shall be afforded for persons to operate, or give attention to, installed equipment;
- Equipment exposed to adverse weather or other corrosive conditions shall be designed to prevent any danger from this;
- No additions to installations shall be made without ascertaining there is sufficient spare capacity for it;
- No additions to installations shall be made without ensuring that the earthing arrangements are adequate;
- Testing shall be carried out on completion of the installation, to the requirements of the IEE Wiring Regulations.

The above requirements are fundamental to ensuring that installations are carried out safely, and are suitable for the purpose that they were installed for, and we shall be returning to them more fully in other sections of the book.

Test 3

Choose which of the four answers is the correct one.

(1) The IEE Wiring Regulations are:

(a) Statutory;
(b) Mandatory;
(c) Bye-laws;
(d) Recommendations.

(2) Which of these is beyond the scope of the IEE Regulations:

(a) Electrical installations in and around buildings;
(b) Caravans and their sites;
(c) Agricultural and horticultural premises;
(d) Coal mines and quarries.

(3) A person touches a live conductor, you must first:

(a) Isolate the person from the supply;
(b) Call for help;
(c) Get a doctor;
(d) Give the person cardiac massage.

(4) The three conditions required for combustion are:

(a) Fuel, heat and a naked flame;
(b) Fuel, heat and oxygen;
(c) Combustible material, heat and a naked flame;
(d) Combustible material, fuel and oxygen.

(5) A carbon dioxide fire extinguisher is colour coded:

(a) Blue;
(b) Green;
(c) Black;
(d) Red.

Chapter 4
The Measurement, Setting Out and Fixing of Equipment

4.1 Measurement and marking out

Bench work

When prefabricating cable trunking or tray, or even the metal support brackets for these items, much of the preparation can be carried out on some form of bench, whether it be a purpose-made one or one you have rigged up temporarily. The work for the most part will consist of the measurement and scribing of lines and angles on the material prior to cutting, and this will have to be done with great care if the finished job is to be accurately assembled.

Essential tools for bench work

Below are some of the tools required to carry out this sort of work. The list shows tools which are essential for this type of work and should be in the possession of most electricians.

Scriber   A scriber is a thin steel bar ground to a fine point, used like a pencil, and is capable of marking most metals used by the electrician.

Fig. 4.1 Try square and scriber in use.

Try square   When cutting trunking or tray into sections, it is essential if the work is to look right that the edges are cut square; that is to say the cross cut is at 90° with the sides of the trunking or tray. The try square enables us to carry out this task. When the square is placed on the work, make certain that it fits tight up to it and is not held off by any dirt or burrs. If this is not done, the square will not be at 90° and the line we draw with the scriber will not be true. The use of both scriber and try square is shown in Fig. 4.1.

Tape measure   For accuracy an engineer would use a steel rule; however, for most purposes, the steel tape measure is sufficiently accurate for the electrician's use. Consisting of a flexible steel tape which is usually marked in both imperial and metric units of measurement, it slides neatly into its case, which is no more than 50 mm × 50 mm in size and fits easily into the pocket. Most of these tapes have a lug at the end, which can be hooked over the ends of work to be measured; the tape is drawn tight and the measurement carefully marked off (see Fig. 4.2).

Centre punch   This is used mainly for marking the spot where the electrician wishes to drill the work, although it can be used to define a line with a row of punch marks where a piece of work is to be cut, particularly if the work is to be welded and a scribed line might be lost. Many pieces of work have been spoiled by the failure of the electrician to use this tool, as high speed drill bits tend to *wander* if the metal is not *centre popped* beforehand.

Desirable tools

Below is a selection of more sophisticated tools which, if you are required to carry out a lot of this type of work, would be found most useful.

Inside callipers   If the accurate measurement of the inside of a pipe or enclosure is required, then the inside calliper must be used. The legs of the calliper are placed inside the work to be measured and extended outwards until a sliding fit is achieved.

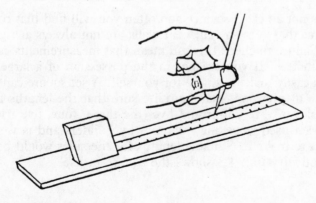

Fig. 4.2 Use of tape measure and scriber.

Outside callipers   Used for accurate measurement of the outside of work, the legs are closed around the work until a sliding fit is achieved. To achieve accurate measurement with both of these callipers, they are taken to a steel rule and the measurement made.

Odd legs callipers   Consisting of one leg like an outside calliper and the other like a scriber, they are used in the opposite way to the above callipers. The measurement is taken off the steel rule first and then the calliper is placed onto the work. The calliper leg is slid along the true edge of the work and the scriber allowed to scribe a mark. Details of the above can be found on Information Sheet No. 4A.

Steel rule   For accurate measurement the steel rule is a must. It is not affected by distortion in the way a steel tape can be, and the marks showing the units of measurement never rub off. It is used with all the tools described above, and provided it is kept lightly oiled will last a lifetime.

Bevel   A bevel or adjustable square can be most useful when marking angles on work. The engineer's version of this tool is marked off in degrees and is most accurate in use.

4.2 Tools and equipment for setting out

The positioning or *setting out* of items of equipment in their correct places on site calls for a certain amount of skill, but the task can be made a lot easier if the correct tools are employed. Below is a list of tools required to carry out this type of work:

- Spirit level;
- Straight edge;
- Plumb/chalk line;
- Try square (large);
- Water level.

Information Sheet No. 4B shows how some of these tools should be employed.

Building is not an exact science and often you will find that rooms are not always square; that is to say adjacent walls are not always at right angles to each other. Failure to check this can mean that measurements can be out by several centimetres. If you are not in the possession of a large try square, then you can easily make a square for yourself. A set square can be cut from a single piece of plywood, making quite sure that the lengths for the sides are in multiples of three, four and five (the three, four, five triangle). This device has been used since ancient times by builders and is well worth the trouble taken to make it. Suitable lengths for the sides would be 30, 40 and 50 cm respectively. Fig. 4.3 shows the square in use.

Information Sheet No. 4A Callipers.

1. Inside callipers used for taking internal dimensions.

2. Odd legs callipers used for marking up work as shown.

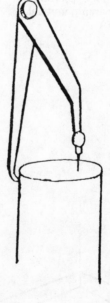

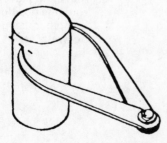

3. Outside callipers used for taking external dimensions.

Information Sheet No. 4B 'Setting Out'.

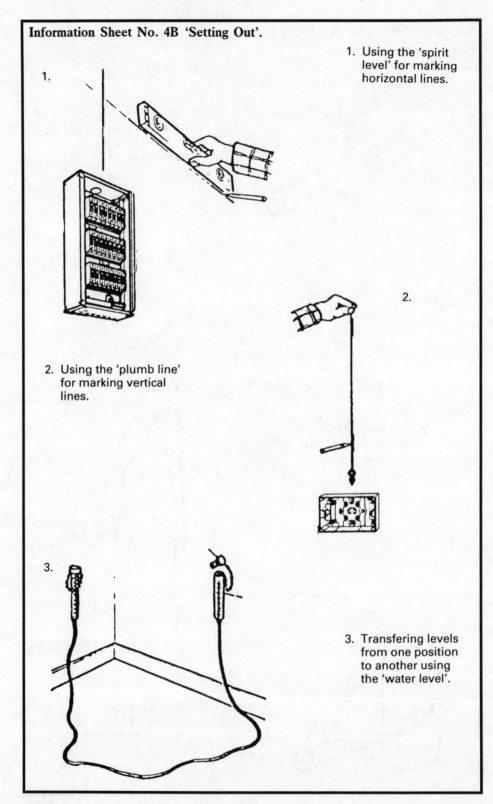

1. Using the 'spirit level' for marking horizontal lines.

2. Using the 'plumb line' for marking vertical lines.

3. Transfering levels from one position to another using the 'water level'.

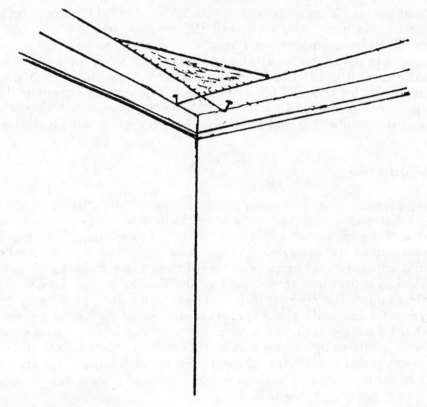

Fig. 4.3 Square in use.

4.3 Fixing methods

Plastic plug and wood screw

Position the article to be fixed using the marking out methods mentioned above. If the article is small, *offer it up* to the wall in the chosen position and mark the position of the fixing holes with a pencil or bradawl.

Remove the article and where the pencil or bradawl have left their mark, make a small cross with the mark at the centre. If the article is large, it will be necessary to measure the fixing centres with your rule and transfer these to the position in which you wish to fix the article. Alternatively, a template can be made from stiff card; the fixing holes are marked on this and it is a simple job to offer this up to the wall instead of the heavy piece of equipment.

Select a suitable sized screw for the size of the article you are going to fix, the bigger the article the larger the size of screw. Most electrical switch, socket and conduit boxes can be fixed with a No. 8 plug and screw. The length of the screw will to some extent depend on the weight of the article to be fixed, also if the masonry is poor you will need to drill a deeper hole to obtain a sound fixing. Use a masonry drill the same size as your choice of screw. These sometimes *wander* a little when you start to drill, but you will be able to re-centre the bit if you have placed a cross on the mark as suggested earlier. It is advisable when fixing electrical switch boxes to always use round-headed screws if the boxes are not counter sunk, otherwise there is a great risk of the conductors being cut on the sharp-edged head of the counter sunk screw. Fig. 4.4 shows the above operation being carried out.

Rawlbolt fixing

Heavy equipment requires something a little more substantial to fix it than the modest plastic plug and screw. The rawlbolt is designed to provide a quick and easy method of achieving heavy duty fixings. There are a number of variations of the fixing, but the two most commonly used are the ones offering either the stud fixing or the bolt fixing. The position of the fixings are marked as described above, and the hole is drilled to suit the size of the rawlbolt in use. The rawlbolt shell, complete with bolt, is placed very carefully into the hole and a check is made to ensure that the hole is the correct depth. At this stage, the bolt is screwed carefully out leaving the shell behind; the work is offered up and the bolt screwed back in. The rawlbolt works on the principle that as the bolt is screwed home the shell expands and grips the sides of the hole, making a secure fixing. Information Sheet No. 4C shows how the bolt fixing type is utilised.

Spring toggle

With today's modern construction methods, electricians find themselves having to fix equipment to walls and ceilings constructed of plasterboard. Normal fixing methods using plastic plugs and screws are of no use. However, a useful device that has been around for many years overcomes this problem; this is the spring toggle. A hole is made in the plaster board a little

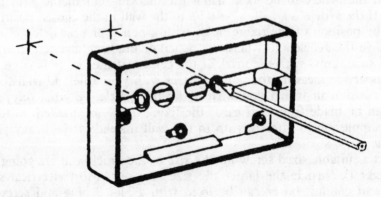

Fig. 4.4 Marking fixing holes.

Information Sheet No. 4C Fixings.

1. Rawlbolt

2. Spring toggle

3. Gravity toggle

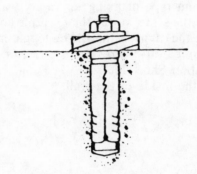

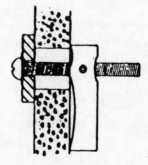

larger than the fixing bolt that is to be used (the toggle comes complete with bolt). The wings of the toggle are folded back against the pressure of a tiny spring and inserted into the hole. When the toggle goes through the hole into the cavity behind, the spring forces the wings outwards. The screw is now tightened up until the fixing is secure. Information Sheet No. 4C shows how this is done.

Gravity toggle

A different type of fixing for cavity walls is the gravity toggle. The hole is made in the same way as the example above and the toggle is passed through and into the cavity behind. The toggle which consists of a hollow plated steel bar mounted off-centre, drops down under the force of gravity, as shown in Information Sheet No. 4C. The bolt is tightened up and the toggle grips against the inside of the wall.

Test 4

Choose which of the four answers is the correct one.

(1) One of the tools listed below is not essential to marking out:

(a) Scriber;
(b) Try square;
(c) Tape measure;
(d) Micrometer.

(2) Which of the following is used for taking internal diameters:

(a) Odd leg callipers;
(b) Outside callipers;
(c) Inside callipers;
(d) Engineers' compasses.

(3) To ensure a conduit drop is vertical, use is made of a:

(a) Plumb line;
(b) Chalk line;
(c) Water level;
(d) Try square.

(4) A spring toggle is suitable for fixing into:

(a) High density concrete;
(b) Plasterboard ceiling;
(c) Brickwork;
(d) Ceramic tiles.

(5) Which of the following is suitable for fixing heavy equipment:

(a) Gravity toggle;
(b) Screw and plastic plug;
(c) Spring toggle;
(d) Rawlbolt.

Chapter 5
The Distribution of Electricity to the Consumer

5.1 Local distribution of electricity

The sub-station

The distribution of electricity at local level is at 11 kV and consists for the main part of small sub-stations often connected together in the form of a ring for additional security of supply. Here the 11 kV three wire supply is stepped down by the use of a *delta-star* transformer to a 415 V four wire supply, with the *star point* connected to earth, as shown in Fig. 5.1.

Distribution of 415/240 V supplies

In the towns and suburban districts, the four wire 415/240 V supplies will be distributed in the form of an underground cable. This three phase and neutral supply, as it is referred to, will be taken directly into the premises of larger users such as small factories, blocks of offices and flats, and large commercial premises. For the smaller consumer only, one of the phases, together with the neutral, will be made available; this is known as a single phase supply (see Fig. 5.1).

The balancing of loads

In an attempt to share the load as evenly as possible over each of the three phases, the local electricity board will connect single phase supplies to each of the phases in turn (see Fig. 5.1). This helps to prevent any one phase being overloaded, thus keeping the size of the cable used to a minimum, reducing the current in the neutral and so keeping distribution costs down. When a three phase and neutral supply is taken into a building, this practice should be continued and the electrician should see to it that the various loads are balanced over the three phases as near as is practical.

5.2 Systems of main intake and earthing connection

The service intake position

The supply authorities' cable is terminated in the form of a service cut-out, as soon as practical after entering the consumer's premises. This equipment

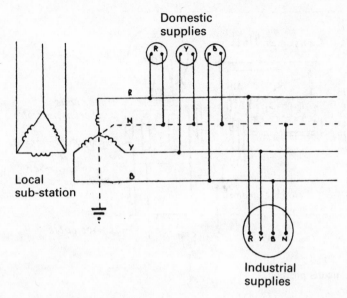

Fig. 5.1 Local distribution.

must contain provision for automatic disconnection of the supply under fault conditions as follows:

(1) Overcurrent (overload or short circuit);
(2) Dangerous earth fault currents.

Protection against these is usually provided in the form of high breaking capacity fuses (HBC), the rating of which will depend on the type of premises being supplied and the size of the service cable. Regulation 4 of the Electricity Supply Regulations 1988 requires one conductor of an AC distribution network to be solidly earthed and therefore this earthed conductor, or neutral as it is known, terminates in a simple terminal block or a removable solid link (see Fig. 5.2).

Methods of system earthing

Electrical supplies entering premises vary slightly with the type of earthing provision adopted. The IEE Wiring Regulations outline five different systems, however, one of these requires special authorisation before use and another cannot be used at all for public supplies. The three most popular systems are shown in Information Sheet No. 5A and it will be noted that the systems are classified with a three or four letter designation; the meaning of which is as follows.

The first letter denotes the supply earthing arrangement:

T – Earth (terre); one or more points connected to earth;
I – All parts isolated from earth or one point connected to earth through a high impedance.

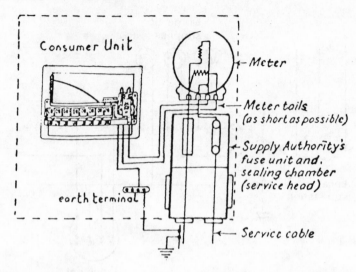

Fig. 5.2 The mains position.

The second letter denotes the installation earthing arrangement:

T – All exposed conductive parts connected directly to earth;
N – All exposed conductive parts connected directly to the earthed conductor (which for AC is usually the neutral).

The third and fourth letters denote the arrangement of neutral and protective conductors:

S – Neutral and protective conductors separate;
C – Neutral and protective conductors combined.

Careful study of these letters and the systems shown in Information Sheet No. 5A will soon make the differences in the systems clear. Prior to the above classification system being introduced, other ways of classifying these conductors were employed and as these classifications are still used by electricity boards and other authorities it would be useful to take a look at these:

PME – This refers to protective multiple earthing (now known as TN–C–S), for which permission for its use is required from the Secretary of State for Energy in England and Wales and the Secretary of State for Scotland north of the border;
PEN – This denotes the combined protective and neutral conductors in the cables supplying the PME system;
CNE – Sometimes the above cable is referred to as combined neutral and earth;
PNB – This stands for protective neutral bonding, used on overhead systems employing individual transformers, where the supply authority will, by agreement, connect an earth electrode at the consumer's premises, as well as at their transformer.

Information Sheet No. 5A Types of earthing systems.

1. TN–S system

   Separate neutral and protective conductors throughout the system.

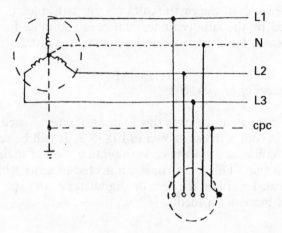

2. TN–C–S system

   Neutral and protective conductors in a single conductor in part of the system.

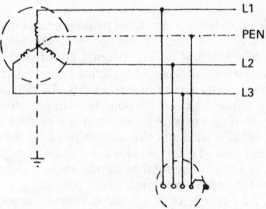

3. TT system

   All exposed conductive parts of an installation are connected to an earth electrode which is electrically independent of the source earth.

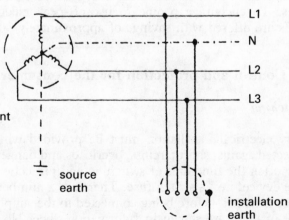

Whichever system is provided, it is the responsibility of the consumer, or the electrical contractor working for him, to satisfy themselves that the characteristics of the earth fault current path, including any part of that path provided by the supply undertaking, are suitable for the effective operation of the earth fault protection chosen for the installation.

The metering of supplies

The electric meter records the amount of energy used in a particular installation; it is connected as shown in Fig. 5.2. It will be seen that the meter has a current coil and a voltage coil; the interaction of their magnetic fields causes a disc to spin. This, in turn, is connected to gears which operate the display, which can be either the dial or digital type; the speed of the disc increases with an increase in load.

Tariffs

The unit of measure is the kilowatt hour and is the result, for example, of a load of 1 kW being used for one hour or 2 kW being used for a half hour. At present, a number of different tariffs are offered by the supply authorities involving various methods of metering. Some of the different arrangements are shown in Information Sheet No. 5B. To calculate the amount of money owing in a domestic installation, the supply authority simply deduct the previous reading on your meter from the present one. This gives them the number of units used and this is multiplied by the cost per unit, to arrive at a total unit cost. To this is added a standing or quarterly charge for provision of the service, the total being the amount to be paid. Special tariffs can be offered to some consumers where consumption can be taken in off-peak periods. An example of this is the *Economy* 7 scheme for domestic users. In the meter, a time-switch operates alternative sets of dials, or switches between separate meters, thus recording energy used at both off-peak and normal times. To encourage people to use off-peak electricity, specially reduced tariffs are offered with savings of approximately 50% on the normal tariff.

5.3 Control and protection for the consumer

Switching

Every electrical installation must be provided with a main switch and be protected against short circuits, overloads and dangerous earth fault currents. Very often the functions of switching and protection are incorporated in the same device, i.e., a switch fuse. There are a number of ways that switchgear can be arranged before being connected to the supply authorities' meters and some of these are shown in Information Sheet No. 5B. For the most part, domestic installations will achieve compliance with the Regulations by use of a consumer control unit made to BS 1454, which combines a double pole

Information Sheet No. 5B Metering and switchgear layouts.

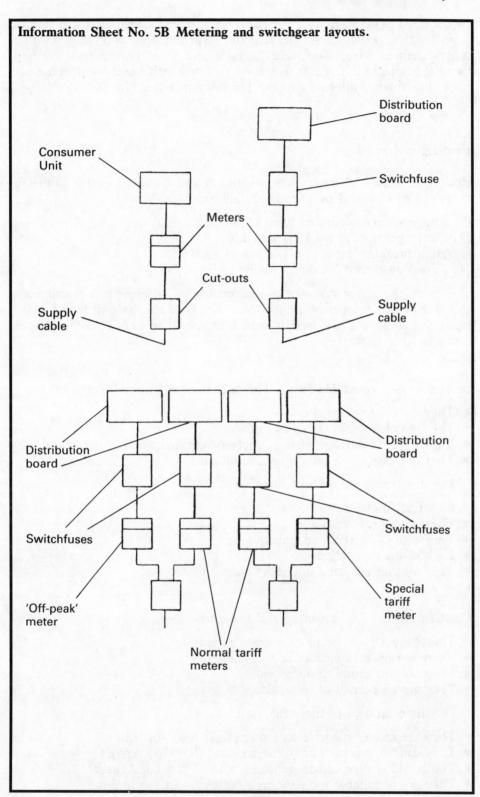

switch rated at 60/80 A with the required number of final circuit fuseways. Care must be taken when installing the insulated version of the consumer control unit as they often have no back and must be mounted on non-flammable material; they can, however, be fitted with a non-flammable back-plate. For further information, see Information Sheet No. 5C.

Protective devices

Protection against short circuits, overloads and dangerous earth fault currents can be obtained by use of the following:

(1) Semi-enclosed rewirable fuses to BS 3036;
(2) Cartridge fuses to BS 1361 and 1362;
(3) High breaking capacity (HBC) fuses to BS 88;
(4) Miniature circuit breakers (MCB) to BS 3871.

Each of the above types of protection are of different construction and this is shown in Information Sheet No. 5D. They also have different advantages and disadvantages, and it would be useful to look at some of these characteristics here.

Semi-enclosed rewirable fuse   The advantages of these fuses are:

- They have a low initial cost;
- The fuse element is cheap to replace;
- They have no moving parts so there is less maintenance necessary;
- They are easy to check if they are intact.

The disadvantages of these fuses are:

- Incorrect fusewire can be used;
- They deteriorate with age;
- They cannot be replaced quickly;
- Lack of discrimination;
- They are not advisable for short circuit protection.

Cartridge fuse   The advantages of these fuses are:

- They have a more accurate current rating;
- There are no moving mechanical parts;
- They are not prone to deterioration;
- They are of a small physical size.

The disadvantages of these fuses are:

- They are more expensive to replace than rewirable fuses;
- They can be shorted out with silver foil (BS 1361 type);
- The BS 1361 type can be replaced with higher rated fuse;
- They are unsuitable for very high fault current conditions.

Information Sheet No. 5C Fixing consumer units.

1. Cut out a slot in the wooden-based unit, wide enough to take the cables involved. Metal units should have the metal KOs removed and bushes fitted.

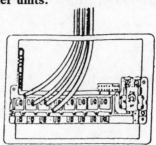

2. Fix the consumer unit to the wall with an approved fixing; strip the cables to within 2 cm of the slotted entry and connect CPCs having fitted green and yellow over sleeve.

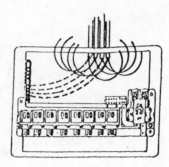

3. Next connect the neutral conductors. It is important that these are in exactly the same order as the phase conductors are going to be.

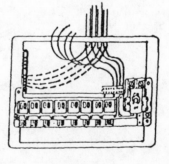

4. Finally connect the phase conductors making sure they are in the same order as the neutral conductors. At all times leave plenty of slack cable.

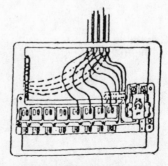

Information Sheet No. 5D Protective devices.

1. High breaking capacity
   fuse (HBC).

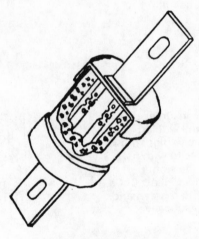

2. Miniature circuit
   breaker (MCB).

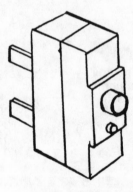

3. Rewirable fuse
   (semi-enclosed).

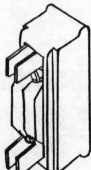

HBC fuse   The advantages of these fuses are:

- There are no moving parts to go wrong or maintain;
- There is no deterioration of the fuse element;
- They are reliable;
- The fuse discriminates between transient and sustained overloads.

The disadvantages of these fuses are:

- They have a high cost;
- It is not always easy to see if the fuse has *blown*.

Miniature circuit breaker   The advantages of these fuses are:

- They are set to a predetermined rating at the factory;
- It is easy to check if the breaker has tripped or not;
- The supply to the circuit is easily reinstated;
- Multi-pole units are available;
- They discriminate between sustained and transient overloads.

The disadvantages of these fuses are:

- They have a high cost;
- They have mechanical moving parts;
- Tripping heavy overloads causes distortion due to heat;
- Ambient temperature affects their characteristics;
- Regular tests are required to ensure their satisfactory operation.

Further work on the above is detailed in Book 2 of the series.

Test 5

Choose which of the four answers is the correct one.

(1) The standard voltage between phases of a three phase supply is:

(a) 230 V;
(b) 240 V;
(c) 415 V;
(d) 500 V.

(2) The double pole switch in a consumer unit provides:

(a) Overload protection;
(b) Short circuit protection;
(c) Isolation;
(d) Correct polarity.

(3) The earthed neutral in the supply authorities' cut-out is:

(a) In the form of a solid link;
(b) Fitted with a single pole switch;
(c) Fitted with a protective device;
(d) Left disconnected.

(4) The letters PME stand for:

(a) Protective mains earthing;
(b) Protective multiple earthing;
(c) Protective mains electrode;
(d) Protective meter earth.

(5) In a domestic premises, charges are usually based upon:

(a) Kilovolt–ampere hours;
(b) Joules per hour;
(c) Coulombs per hour;
(d) Kilowatt hours.

Chapter 6
The Installation of Wiring Systems

6.1 The installation of PVC/PVC wiring systems

Reasons for choice

Polyvinyl chloride is tough, cheap, easy to work with and install, so it is not surprising, therefore, to find that the PVC insulated/PVC sheathed cable is the most popular type of cable in current use. This form of insulation has its limitations in conditions of excessive heat or cold, and can be subject to mechanical damage unless given additional mechanical protection in certain situations. However, provided this and the other factors mentioned later are taken into consideration, the PVC/PVC wiring system is probably the most versatile of all the wiring systems.

Stripping

This type of cable comes in various forms and the more common types are shown on Information Sheet No. 6A. The stripping of PVC/PVC cables is generally done with a knife. The knife should be sharp and held at a very acute angle to the cable, so that the insulation is pared rather than cut. To cut at a near right angle would be very bad practice because, although it may give a neater finish, it would probably result in the nicking of the insulation or conductor. A nicked conductor becomes so weak that, after having been bent a few times, it will almost certainly break. Apart from this tendency to break, the effective cross-sectional area of the conductor will be reduced, causing increased resistance which may result in excessive heat. Techniques used in the stripping of these cables in this way are shown in Information Sheet No. 6B.

Terminating

The entry of a cable end into an accessory is known as the *termination* of the cable. In the case of a stranded conductor, the strands should be twisted together with pliers before terminating. Care should be taken that this is not overdone, as it may result in damage to the conductors. The IEE Wiring Regulations require that a cable termination of any kind shall securely anchor all the wires of the conductor and shall not impose any appreciable mechanical stress on the terminal or socket.

A termination under mechanical stress is liable to disconnection. When

Information Sheet No. 6A Types of cable.

1. PVC insulated
   PVC sheathed
   two core and CPC

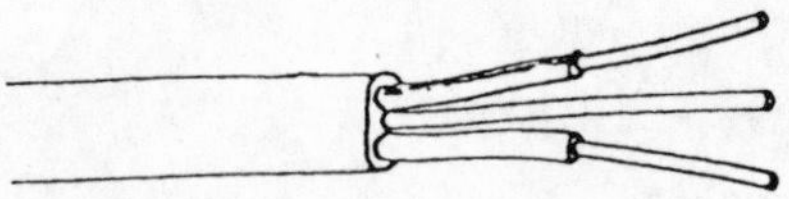

2. PVC insulated
   PVC sheathed
   two core cable

3. PVC insulated
   twin bell wire

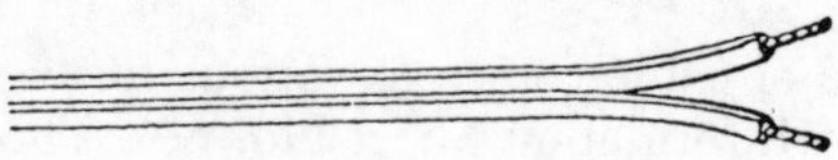

4. PVC/SWA/PVC
   armoured cable

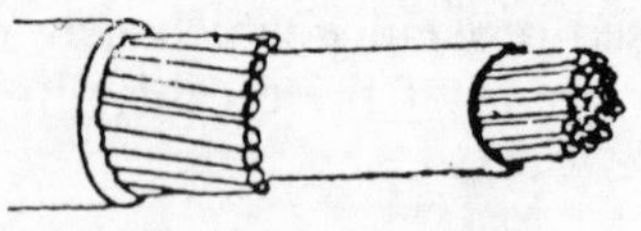

Information Sheet No. 6B Stripping PVC cables.

1. Nick the cable at the end with your knife and pull apart as shown.

2. When the required length has been stripped, cut off the surplus sheathing with the knife as shown.

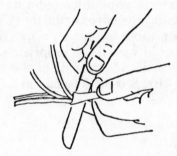

3. The insulation can be stripped from the conductors with the knife as shown.

4. An alternative method of stripping the insulation from the conductors is with a pair of purpose-made strippers as shown.

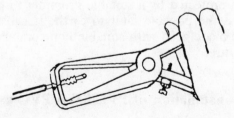

current is flowing, a certain amount of heat is developed, and the consequent expansion and contraction may be sufficient to allow the conductor under stress, particularly tension, to be pulled out of the terminal or socket.

If one or more strands, or wires, are left out of the terminal or socket, there would be a reduction in the effective csa of the conductor at that point. This would mean increased resistance and probably overheating; in addition to this, any strands left sticking out would be potentially dangerous. Typical types of terminal used in electrical installation work are shown in Information Sheet No. 6C.

The cable sheath of this type of wiring system is provided to give the cable mechanical protection. It is important, therefore, that this protection is maintained throughout the installation, by ensuring that the sheath enters the accessory or enclosure. If, for any reason, termination to a piece of equipment requires removal of this sheath outside the enclosure, then additional mechanical protection should be provided.

There are a number of different forms of this type of cable, many of which include a circuit protective conductor (CPC). This CPC is not insulated and therefore when cables of this type are terminated, the protective conductor should be sleeved with the appropriate sized yellow-and-green striped PVC over the sleeve. Further details of the identification of conductors can be found in the IEE Wiring Regulations 524–1, 2 and 3.

Installation

The general installation of these cables should present no difficulty, provided the above factors are taken into consideration, and the techniques used are shown in Information Sheet No. 6D. When cables are installed above ceilings or under floors, they should be run in such a way as not to be damaged by floor or ceiling boards or their fixings (IEE Regulations 523–20). If the cable cannot be run through joists at a distance of 50 mm or more from the top or bottom of the joist, then they should be mechanically protected in such a way as to prevent nails, screws and the like penetrating them. Where these cables are installed under cement or plaster, they should be contained in a suitably bushed piece of conduit, or alternatively covered with a piece of metal or plastic channel. Where cables enter metal enclosures, the entry should be protected by a suitable grommet to prevent abrasion of the cable sheath and the possible fault to earth. If cables pass through walls, these should be made good with suitable non-combustible material to prevent the spread of fire.

6.2 The installation of PVC/SWA/PVC cables

Reasons for choice

We have seen in Chapter 3 that all cables to be installed underground shall have built into them a sheath or armouring able to resist mechanical damage; the PVC insulated steel wire armoured PVC sheathed cable is just such a

Information Sheet No. 6C Types of terminals.

1. Typical PVC
   insulated
   connector block

2. Stud terminal
   using a nut and
   washers

3. Screw and washer
   connection

4. Terminal post
   connection

 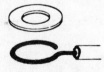

5. Claw washers used mainly
   on light conductors or flexibles

Information Sheet No. 6D Installation of PVC cables.

1. Typical examples
   of clips used to
   fasten PVC cables.
   They come in all
   sizes to suit
   the different
   cables and cross-sections.

2. The cable can be
   straightened by
   running the thumb
   over it before clipping.
   The palm of the hand
   can be used for the
   bigger cables.

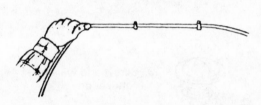

3. A cross-pane
   hammer will be
   found to be
   the most usful
   type to employ.

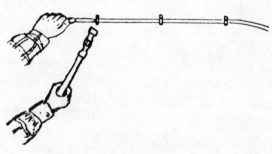

4. The clips should
   be placed at
   equal distances
   apart and these,
   and the radius of the
   curve, can be found in
   the IEE Regulations.

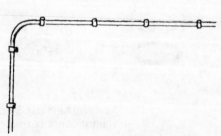

cable. This cable comes in a number of forms and one of the most popular types is shown in Fig. 6.1, together with the cable gland used for terminating the cable. Its use is not limited to underground installations, however, as the added protection afforded by the sheath makes it ideally suitable for those industrial or commercial situations where mechanical protection is of paramount importance.

Terminating

The cable consists of PVC insulated conductors with an overall covering of PVC. Between this covering and the outer PVC sheath is embedded the galvanised steel wire armouring. The armouring is used as a protective conductor and special glands are employed to ensure good continuity between this and the metalwork of the equipment to which we are connecting. These glands vary a little from one manufacturer to another and their design also depends on the environment in which they are to be used. Details of how to terminate the cable, using a gland designed for indoor use, are given in Information Sheet No. 6E.

Start by measuring the length of armouring required to fit over the cable clamp; note the measurement. Then establish how long the conductors need

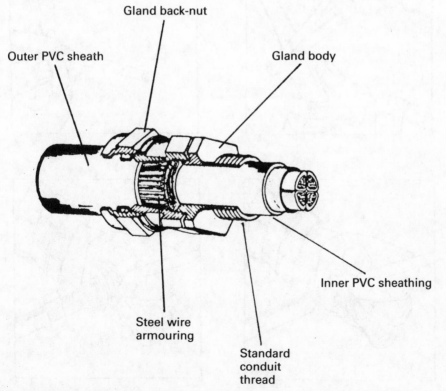

Fig. 6.1 Section of PVC/SWA/PVC cable and gland.

Information Sheet No. 6E Terminating PVC/SWA/PVC cables.

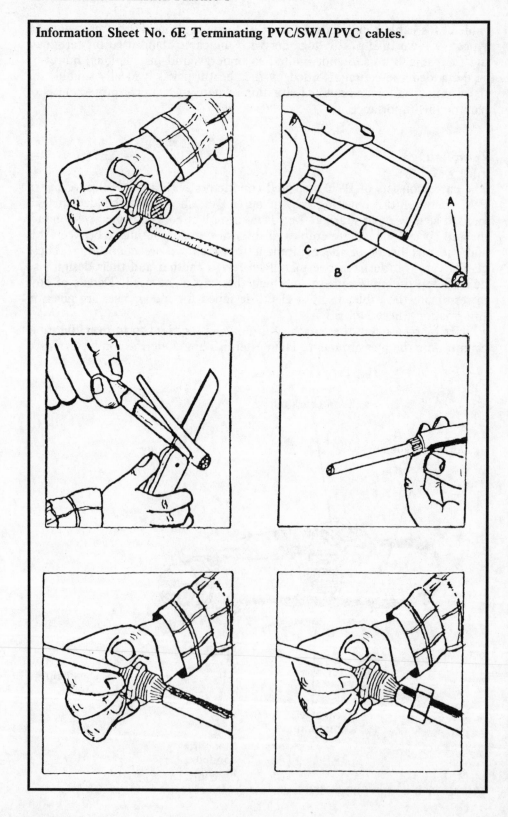

to be in order to connect your equipment; make a note of this. Taking the cable, measure from the end of the cable marked A in drawing No. 2 to position B; this represents the length of the conductors required. Follow this by marking the length required for the cable clamp from B to C, as shown on the drawing. At this stage, some people will strip off the PVC outer sheath; however, this is best left on as it will hold the steel wire armouring in place for you.

Next, taking a junior hacksaw, cut through the PVC outer sheath and partly through the armouring at point B; the PVC outer sheath can now be cut away as shown in drawing No. 3. Taking each strand of the armouring in turn, snap them off at the point where they are partly cut through. Then, either using the hacksaw or a knife, cut neatly round the PVC outer sheath at point C and remove the remaining piece of outer sheath; this will leave the cable as shown in drawing No. 4. The gland can now be fitted onto the cable. First slide the backnut and compression rings, if any, onto the cable. Then, taking the gland body, slide this onto the cable, making sure that it fits under all the strands of armouring as shown in drawing No. 5.

Finally, slide up the backnut and screw it onto the gland body, thus clamping the armouring tightly. The inner PVC sheath can be stripped off like any other PVC cable and the gland is ready for connection to your equipment. It is important that good contact is made by cleaning any paint work off the area of contact before tightening up the lock nut securing the gland. Bonding rings, or earthing tags as they are sometimes called, can be used to provide better contact with surrounding metalwork.

Installation

Installation is relatively easy for the smaller size cables, but it will become necessary to employ an installation team to handle the bigger sizes or multi-core cables. For the most part, *one-hole* cable cleats constructed of solid PVC will be used as shown in Fig. 6.2, or in the case of cables installed on cable tray, cable ties will be utilised (see Fig. 6.3) For the bigger cables, cleats made of diecast aluminium are used. These are often designed to be slotted into steel channels so that, once a piece of channel has been fixed, multiple runs of cable can be accommodated. The minimum radius that these cables should be bent to is eight times the outside diameter, and the spacing of

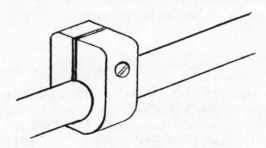

Fig. 6.2 Cable cleat.

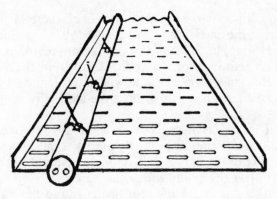

Fig. 6.3 Cable ties.

the cleats should be as recommended in Table 11A of the IEE Regulations. Where these cables are to be installed directly into the ground, they should be marked with cable covers or suitable PVC marking tape to indicate their presence. They should be buried at a sufficient depth to avoid their being damaged by any disturbance of the ground reasonably likely to occur during normal use of the premises.

6.3 The installation of mineral insulated metal sheathed cables

Reasons for choice

When the ambient temperature in which cables are to be installed is high, it is difficult for the heat generated by the flow of current through the cables to be dispersed. This can result in the melting of the insulation, if adequate care is not taken to reduce the current carrying capacity of the cable. PVC insulated cables in particular suffer in this respect; however, magnesium oxide is able to withstand high degrees of temperature when used as an insulation for cables. Mineral insulated metal sheathed (MIMS) cables use magnesium oxide as their insulation, and this, together with the fact that they have a metal sheath, means that they are ideally suitable for installations where the ambient temperatures are high. These attributes are also made use of in installations where there is a high risk of fire, or in security systems, such as fire alarms and emergency lighting, where it would be desirable for the system to work for as long as possible under fire conditions.

Types of cable

The cable can be obtained with copper or aluminium sheaths; however, by far the most commonly used type is the one with copper conductors and copper sheaths (MICC). For outdoor use, or if the cable has to be run under the ground, the cable can be obtained with an over sheathing of PVC. This PVC over sheathing is also impervious to many oil and chemical products, so this makes it ideally suitable for installations such as petrol filling stations. There are two grades of cable, light duty rated up to 600 V; this is used for domestic and light duty work, and heavy duty rated up to 1000 V, which is used for industrial and other heavy duty applications. Both these cables can carry higher currents for the same cable size than other types of cable. The heavy duty cable carries a little higher current (see IEE Wiring Regulations Tables 9J1 and 9J3) because of its ability to disperse heat more quickly, due to its thicker outer sheath.

Termination

Magnesium oxide powder is highly hygroscopic; that is to say it absorbs moisture readily. The cable is therefore terminated using a brass pot into which is pressed a plastic compound, in order to seal the end and prevent the ingress of moisture. Should dampness enter the cable for any reason, it will only be necessary to strip back a short length of the cable to restore it to normal. If a situation arises where dampness enters the cable and it is not convenient to strip the cable back, then the pot should be removed and a blow lamp played on the end of the cable. This is most effective if the flame is started some 150 mm from the end of the cable and gradually worked to the end, thus driving out the moisture. The method used to strip and terminate the cable is shown in Information Sheet No. 6F. A number of proprietary stripping tools are now available on the market and one of the most popular types is shown in Fig. 6.4. A gland is used in conjunction with the pot when terminating the cable into equipment. It comes in three separate parts: (1) the gland body which has a standard electrical thread, usually 20 mm for the smaller cables and 25 mm for the larger (2) an olive or compression ring, which tightens onto the cable thus affording good continuity and (3) the backing nut which tightens down onto the olive when the gland has been positioned correctly.

Installation

The cable is very malleable and can be bent and shaped without damage; however, like all metals, if it is *worked* too much, it will eventually fracture. It is capable of withstanding hard blows and still be operational, although mechanical protection should be provided where there is danger of damage, particularly from sharp objects. We learned earlier how *mechanical stress* can cause the breakdown of cables and that one of the causes is vibration. This can be avoided in MIMS installations if the cable is taken round in a small loop before connection to equipment, especially motors or plant likely to vibrate (see Fig. 6.5). This has the added advantage of allowing the motor or equipment to be moved a little for final adjustment, or tensioning of the belt drive.

   The small overall diameter of the cable means that it can be installed under plaster without having to chase the walls, thus saving on installation costs, although PVC served cable should be used to avoid interaction between the

Information Sheet No. 6F MIMS terminations.

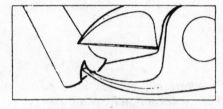

1. Start stripping the MIMS cable with the side cutters.

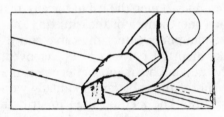

2. Curl off about 2 cm of cable sheath.

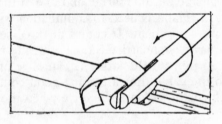

3. Insert the section of sheath into the slot of the stripping rod.

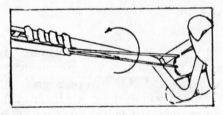

4. 'Turn off' enough sheath to allow the conductors to be correct length.

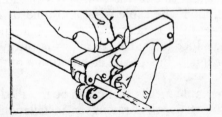

5. Place a ringing tool onto the cable and turn this to form a groove.

Information Sheet No. 6G MIMS terminations continued.

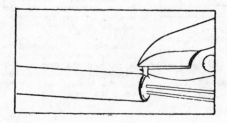

6. Snap off the surplus sheath and clean up the end of the cable.

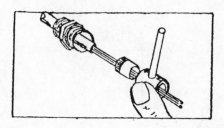

7. The cable is now ready to receive a pot using the potting tool.

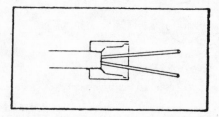

8. The end of the cable should reach the 'shoulders' of the pot as shown.

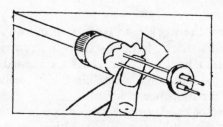

9. Fill the pot from one side using plastic compound.

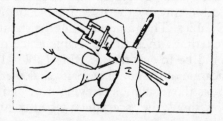

10. Finally slide on the stub cap and crimp it in position as shown.

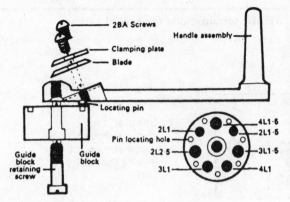

2BA Screws

Handle assembly

Clamping plate

Blade

Locating pin

Guide block retaining screw

Guide block

2L1
Pin locating hole
2L2·5
3L1

4L1·6
2L1·5
3L1·5
4L1

SETTING THE GUIDE BLOCK
Unscrew the guide block retaining screw, recessed in the back of the guide block, in order to clear the block from the locating pin in the handle assembly. The block can then be rotated to fit the appropriate cable sizes and the locating pin engaged. *FINGER PRESSURE ONLY TO BE USED*. Do not force the guide block by tightening the retaining screw. Ensure no dirt is blocking the locating hole. Then tighten the retaining screw and the tool is ready. Do not adjust the blade.

Fig. 6.4 Stripping tool for MIMS cable.

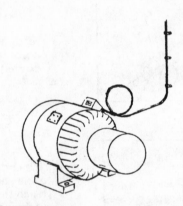

Fig. 6.5 Expansion loop in MIMS cable.

bare copper and the finishing plaster. If the work is to be carried out on the surface, it is so neat and inconspicuous that it lends itself to the rewiring of buildings, such as churches and other historic edifices. As mentioned in Chapter 3, care should be taken to avoid situations where electrolytic action can take place and, in particular, where moisture is about.

The cable is usually fixed by the use of *one-hole* clips which can be either bare copper or PVC covered, to suit the cable being used. Other types of fixings, such as saddles, spacer-bar saddles and perforated strip, can be obtained and the cable can be fixed to cable tray by the use of cable ties in much the same way as PVC/SWA/PVC cables. The minimum internal radius that the cable should be bent to is six times the outside diameter of the cable, and the spacing of the clips should be in accordance with Table 11A of the IEE Wiring Regulations. Identification of the conductors is particularly important in this type of wiring system, as the insulation sleeving provided is all black in colour. Polarity of the cables should be ascertained when testing is carried out and the cables marked accordingly.

6.4 The installation of conduit wiring systems

Steel conduit and the reasons for choice

Steel conduit is one of the most popular systems of wiring for commercial and industrial premises and has a number of advantages over other wiring systems. It affords excellent mechanical protection of cables, so it is entirely suitable for installations in production plants, workshops and those types of installations where the installation is subjected to a certain amount of hard use. Rewiring of this system is reasonably straightforward and circuits can be added or removed with comparative ease. Many modern buildings are constructed of in situ concrete and the conduits can be installed in the shuttering prior to the pouring of the concrete; this results in a completely concealed installation which can be wired after removal of the shuttering. Because the system is enclosed in steel throughout, it minimises risk of fire, and if certain equipment and accessories are used, it can, in fact, be used in high risk areas. When installed correctly, with all bushes and couplings correctly tightened, the steel conduit can be used as the protective conductor for the circuit, thus saving on cable.

Disadvantages of the steel conduit is that it is quite expensive compared to some other wiring systems; it requires a certain amount of skill in its installation and is therefore labour intensive. It is liable to corrosion when exposed to acid or alkaline conditions and, under certain conditions, moisture can form on the inside of the conduit, resulting in corrosion or dangerous fault conditions.

Types of steel conduit

The most popular finish for steel conduit is black enamel; however, it can be obtained in galvanised finish which makes it suitable for outdoor use, or situations subject to dampness such as dairies or bottling plants. Conduit with a coating of PVC on the outside surface can be ordered specially for use in situations subject to corrosion, although this is not seen so much since the production of plastic conduit, which we will deal with later.

The steel conduit used on the majority of installations at the present time is of the *heavy gauge* type; this comes in two variations, either the *solid drawn* or the *welded* type. The solid drawn conduit is extruded in the form of a continuous seamless tube, while the welded type is made from sheet steel rolled into a tube and welded along the seam. This welding is done so well that it is hard to tell the difference between this and the solid drawn type; however, a slight ridge can be felt on the inside of the welded type. The solid drawn conduit is more expensive than the welded type and its use is therefore limited to special situations such as gas-proof or flame-proof installations. Both types come in sizes of 16, 20 and 32 mm diameters, and in 3.75 m lengths.

Over the years, *light gauge* conduits have appeared in various forms; at the present time, their use is limited to the protection of sheathed cables from mechanical damage. They are either round or oval in shape and are formed from sheet steel, which is not welded at the seam, and they are not regarded as being suitable for use as protective conductors.

Steel conduit installations

The conduit wiring system consists of two distinct parts: (1) the conduit itself, and (2) the conductors or cables which it contains. The IEE Wiring Regulations make it quite clear that any conduit that is to be installed in situ must be fully erected before any cables are drawn into it, so it would be useful to look at this aspect of the installation first.

Installation of the conduit

First and foremost, the conduit is a metal enclosure for the protection from mechanical damage of the cables to be installed in it, therefore it should be installed in such a way as to afford continuous protection for the cables, and allow the safe and easy installation or withdrawal of such cables. Secondly, because the mass of steel used in the construction of heavy gauge conduit is of sufficiently low resistivity to comply with the recommendations contained in Regulation 543–9 of the IEE Wiring Regulations, it can be used as a protective conductor. It is because of this that it is essential that joints formed by couplings, bushes or accessories in a conduit wiring system are carried out in such a manner as to ensure mechanical and electrical continuity throughout its length. It is these two main points that concern us when considering the installation of steel conduits, so it may be useful to examine some of the requirements for these to ensure a safe and sound installation.

- Conduit ends should be cut squarely; use a pipe vice similar to the one shown on Information Sheet No. 6H;
- Any burrs should be removed either with a round file or a reamer, like the one shown on Information Sheet No. 6H;
- They should be threaded correctly, using stocks and dies, see Information Sheet No. 6H;
- The radius should be bent not less than 2.5 times the diameter of the conduit;
- Limited use should be made of solid elbows or tees (see Regulation 529–4);
- All entries into enclosures should be correctly bushed;
- Correct space factors should be applied to the number of cables installed;
- Recommendations regarding fire barriers should be taken into consideration;
- Unused conduit entries should be blanked off;
- Drainage holes should be provided to avoid collection of condensation;
- Conduits should be fixed in accordance with Table 11c of the IEE Regulations;
- All covers and box lids should be in place and securely fastened;
- All recommendations regarding corrosion should be taken into consideration;
- All bushes, couplings and accessories should be securely tightened.

Information Sheet No. 6H Conduit tools.

1. Reamer—used to
clean out 'burrs'
from the inside of
steel conduit.

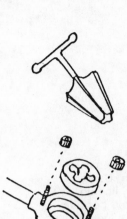

2. Stocks and dies—
used for threading
steel conduit.
Available for all
conduit sizes.

3. Stand vice—a
vice specially designed
for holding pipe or
conduit while cutting
or threading. The
jaws are curved to
help prevent the work
slipping.

4. Bending machine—
by changing the
formers, these machines
can be used to bend
all the popular sizes
of conduit.

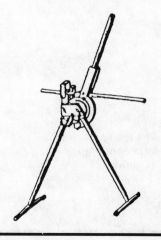

Information Sheet No. 6I Bending conduit.

1. Measure from the
   fixed point to
   the back of the
   bend as in
   'd'. Place in
   the bending machine
   as shown. Using
   a square, line up
   the marked position
   with the edge of
   the former.

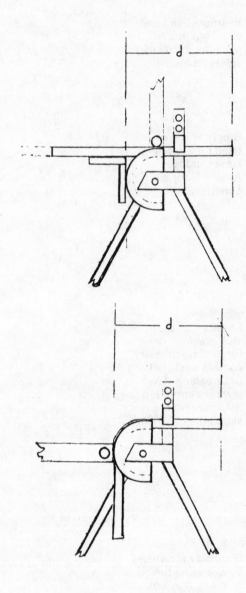

2. Bring the arm of
   the machine
   down, checking
   from the side until
   90° is reached.

3. The result should
   be a right angle
   as shown.

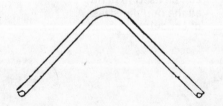

Information Sheet No. 6J Terminating steel conduit.

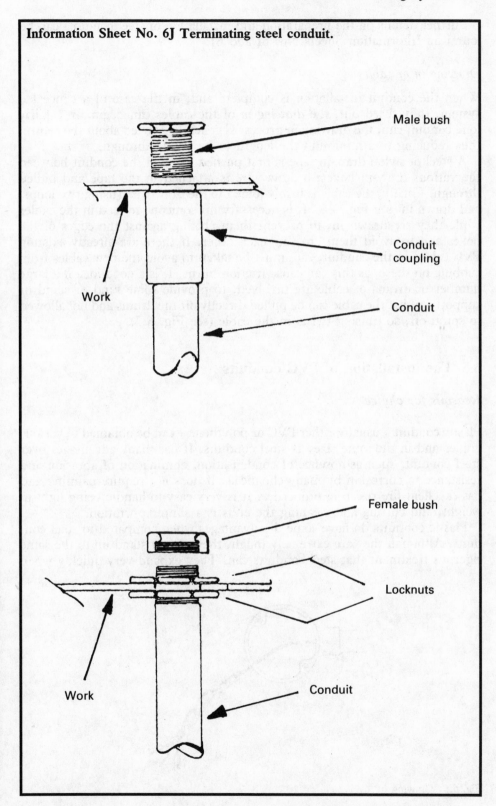

Male bush

Conduit coupling

Work

Conduit

Female bush

Locknuts

Work

Conduit

Further details on the preparation and installation of steel conduits can be found on Information Sheets Nos 6I and 6J.

Drawing in of cables

When the conduit installation is complete and, in the case of a concealed system, fully dried out, the *drawing in* of the cables can begin. In a fairly long conduit run, the drawing in process is generally started about the centre, thus reducing to a minimum the length to be pulled through.

A steel or nylon draw-in tape is first pushed through the conduit between the various draw-in boxes; a draw wire is attached to the tape and pulled through. Finally, the cable is firmly joined to the draw wire (using two loops) and drawn in (see Fig. 6.6). It is necessary for someone to feed in the cables while they are drawn in, to prevent them chafing against the edges of the boxes and to avoid them crossing each other. If there are already existing PVC cables in the conduit, care must be taken to avoid the new cables from rubbing on these, as this can cause friction burns. It is a good idea if a large number of drums of cable are involved, to provide some kind of stand or support, so that the cable can be pulled directly off the drums and not allowed to spiral off, so causing twists in the cable (see Fig. 6.7).

6.5 The installation of PVC conduits

Reasons for choice

Plastic conduit – usually either PVC or polythene – can be obtained in various grades and in the same sizes as steel conduits. It has many advantages over steel conduit, such as absence of condensation, elimination of abrasion and resistance to corrosion by many chemicals, it does not require painting and has excellent fire resisting properties. It is very easy to handle being light in weight, and cutting and cleaning the ends is a simple operation.

Plastic conduits do have some disadvantages when compared to steel conduits. Although they are extremely tough, they cannot stand up to the same rigorous treatment that steel conduits can. They expand very quickly when

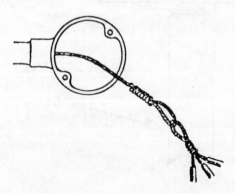

Fig. 6.6 'Drawing in' cables.

Fig. 6.7 'Running off' cables.

exposed to heat, so this must be allowed for when installing them in situations where this may arise. To achieve a neat appearance, they require more saddles on long runs or sagging may take place. Plastic conduits cannot, of course, be used as protective conductors, so these will take the form of additional cables and will have to be taken into account when working out space factors.

Types of plastic conduit

Super high impact This type comes in heavy gauge and light gauge. The heavy gauge is suitable for use in severe weather conditions, while the light gauge is used for in situ concrete work.

Standard impact Probably the most popular of the plastic conduits, it is used on installations where there are no special requirements for weather or excessive heat.

Heavy gauge high temperature Where plastic conduits are to be installed in conditions of high ambient temperature (80–85°C), then this conduit should be used.

Flexible conduit (BS 4607) This is available in both heavy gauge and light gauge. The heavy gauge, which is available in 25 m lengths, is suitable for either sunk or surface work. The light gauge is similar to the above, but has thinner walls.

Oval conduit and capping   Oval conduit and capping is mainly used in domestic installation, to afford protection to cables buried under plaster.

Installation of plastic conduits

Conduits made of PVC are easy to work with compared to the steel type. They can be cut by the use of a junior hack-saw held in the hand and do not require the use of a vice. Burrs are easily removed by inserting the end of your sidecutters into the tube and twisting. It is so light that it can easily be installed by one person working on their own. All the types of conduit boxes and accessories manufactured for steel conduit are available for PVC conduit, although, of course, they are also made from PVC. Plastic conduits are not threaded in the same way as steel ones, so there is no need for stocks and dies, etc. Jointing is a push fit and the end of the tube is coated with PVC solvent adhesive before inserting into the accessory. Care should be taken with this, as if it is done badly surplus adhesive may be squeezed into the tube and form a bridge, making it difficult to draw your cables in later. Make sure the adhesive is spread all round the end of the tube, or water may enter into the conduit and cause problems. A good way to ensure an even distribution of adhesive is to twist the accessory box round, so spreading it evenly.

PVC conduits of 20 mm and 25 mm sizes can be bent with the use of a steel spring, in much the same way that plumbers bend their copper pipes. The spring is inserted into the conduit with a slight twist in the direction that tightens the spring. When you have positioned it at the spot at which you wish to make the bend, it is placed across the knee or, in the case of a young person, across the thigh as their knee makes too tight a bend. Both hands should pull evenly and the bend should be taken past the angle which you wish to obtain, as PVC conduit has a tendency to spring back a little after you take the pressure off. If the tube is of greater length than the spring which you are using, tie string or a piece of cable onto it before making the bend; this will help you recover the spring afterwards, see Fig. 6.8. It may be necessary to heat the PVC conduit a little in cold weather to assist bending. Rubbing vigorously with a dry cloth is usually sufficient to produce enough heat to do the job, although hot water or the heat from a radiator can both be used to good effect. Special heaters are now on the market for use with PVC conduits and are most useful especially for the larger sizes of conduit.

We have seen that plastic conduits are subject to expansion if installed in high ambient temperature; where this is unavoidable, certain techniques can be used to minimise the problem. In long runs of conduit in these conditions, expansion couplers can be used. These should be lightly greased to keep them watertight and fitted with one coupler for every 6 m of run. More saddles are used than with steel conduit and these should be a slide fit to allow expansion to take place without buckling. The joints in high ambient temperature conditions should be made with a non-setting adhesive, which as well as allowing expansion makes a weatherproof joint. As the plastic softens with heat, care should be taken if mounting luminaires on to accessory boxes, especially the types which generate quite a bit of heat. In such cases,

Fig. 6.8 Bending PVC conduit.

the temperature should not exceed 60°C and the luminaire should not weigh in excess of 3 kg.

Safety precautions should be taken with the adhesives, as they are highly inflammable and should not be left near heat. They should be stored in a place which is not accessible to young children, as they can be the subject of abuse in the form of glue sniffing.

6.6 Flexible conduits

Reasons for choice

There are many types of flexible conduits available at the present time, but they all have one common purpose and that is to provide a flexible connection between our permanent installation and some form of equipment. There are two main reasons for wanting a flexible connection: (1) to allow movement to take place of the equipment which we are connecting up, for example, to allow an electric motor to be moved onto its slide rails, in order to tighten up a vee belt drive or (2) to prevent the transmission of vibrations to other .parts of the plant.

Types of flexible conduit

Metallic flexible conduit   This consists of a light gauge galvanised steel strip spirally wound and, to some extent, interlocked, so as to form a tube. It is made in all the popular sizes and can be obtained in both watertight and non-watertight versions.

Plastic flexible conduit   This consists of a steel wire spiral covered overall by PVC. This forms a corrugated effect and makes the conduit very flexible

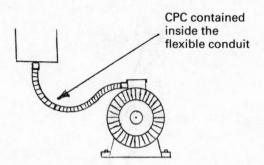

CPC contained
inside the
flexible conduit

Fig. 6.9 Flexible conduit to motor.

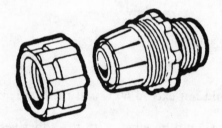

Fig. 6.10 Connector for flexible conduit.

indeed. Plastic flexible conduit too is available in all the popular sizes and is obtainable in 50 m coils.

Reinforced flexible conduit   This is a heavy duty double walled conduit with spiral wire reinforcement. It can be obtained in a number of different types to suit various applications.

Installation

Metallic flexible conduits are connected to equipment by means of special adapters, which are internally rifled at one end so as to screw onto the steel spiral; at the other end of the adapter is a standard conduit thread. Although made of steel, metallic conduits are not regarded as being suitable to act as protective conductors, so therefore an additional cable must be installed to act as a CPC in accordance with Regulation 543–11 (see Fig. 6.9).

Terminating plastic flexible conduits is a simple operation, provided that the correct adapter is obtained for the type of flexible conduit you are using. These often have a coloured PVC insert, which is a different colour for each type of conduit. Most of the adapters work on the principle of inserting a slightly tapered piece into the conduit's inside, then screwing on a back-nut which effectively grips the flexible conduit firmly. Care should be taken when cutting the conduit to ensure a clean cut, otherwise difficulty may be experienced with inserting the tapered piece into the flexible conduit. A clean cut will also make it easier to slip the back-nut onto the conduit before you start the operation. A typical flexible conduit adapter is shown in Fig. 6.10.

Test 6

Choose which of the four answers is the correct one.

(1) The letters PVC stand for:

(a) Plastic vinyl covering;
(b) Poly vinyl chloride;
(c) Poly vinyl covering;
(d) Poly vinyl chlorine.

(2) The cable sheath of PVC insulated and sheathed cable is to:

(a) Provide mechanical protection;
(b) Keep the conductors together;
(c) Give a neat appearance;
(d) Prevent corrosion.

(3) MIMS cables absorb moisture easily. This attribute is termed:

(a) Hydrochloric;
(b) Hygroscopic;
(c) Hydropathic;
(d) Hygrometric.

(4) When installing flexible conduit to equipment:

(a) The cables should be pulled in together;
(b) The gland should be tight for good continuity;
(c) A separate CPC should be installed;
(d) The end of the conduit should be square.

(5) Before pulling cables into the conduit the conduit should be:

(a) Given a coat of paint;
(b) Checked to see that it is level;
(c) Have its continuity checked;
(d) Completely erected.

Chapter 7
Installing Lighting and Small Power Circuits

7.1 The installation of lighting circuits

Final circuits

Electrical apparatus is connected by cables to the electricity supply, and to the associated protective and controlling devices (usually fuses and switches). This arrangement of cables is known as a *circuit* and circuits which connect current, using apparatus to the consumer unit or distribution board, are called *final circuits*.

Lighting final circuits

One of the earliest commercial uses for electricity was for the lighting of premises; indeed, some of the early installations had only lighting installed, as the number of electrical appliances were few.

The simplest lighting circuit is one lamp controlled by one switch and is known as a one-way circuit (see Fig. 7.1). The circuit commences at the protective device in the consumer unit, which is connected to the phase conductor of the supply. From here it goes to the switch controlling the circuit and from there to the lamp. From the lamp the cable returns to the consumer unit where it is connected to the neutral terminal of the consumer unit, so completing the circuit.

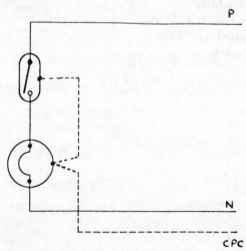

Fig. 7.1 One-way lighting circuit.

When additional lighting points are required, it would be very wasteful to connect each lighting point by its own cables to the consumer unit, therefore the original circuit is extended as shown in Fig. 7.2. This circuit now has two lamps, both of which are controlled by one switch.

If the lamps were required to be switched independently from each other, it would be necessary to extend the circuit as shown in Fig. 7.3. It will be noted that in all cases the circuit protective conductor (shown in dotted lines) is connected to all switch and lamp positions; this is a requirement of the IEE Wiring Regulations.

Two-way lighting circuits

For independent control from two positions, for example on a staircase, two-way switches are required. These switches have three terminals, one of which is called the *common* and is marked with a letter *c*; the other two are called the *strappers* and are usually marked L1 and L2 respectively. A simple two-way circuit is shown in (a) of Information Sheet No. 7A. It will be seen that the neutral conductor is taken to the lamp position. From the other side of the lamp, a conductor known as the switch wire is taken to the common of the second switch, and the two switches are linked by a pair of conductors known as the strappers. From the common of the first switch, a conductor known as the switch feed is taken to the phase.

With the switches in the positions shown in drawing (a), the current travels from the common of the first switch across the switch contacts to L2. From L2 it travels along the L2 strapper to the L2 terminal of the second switch; here it cannot go any further because the contacts of the second switch are open, so that the lamp does not light.

To make the lamp light, it would be necessary for someone to operate switch one so that the common is in contact with L1, as shown in drawing

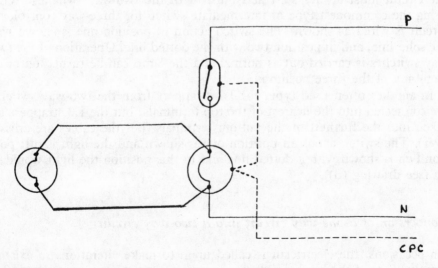

Fig. 7.2 Two lamps controlled by one one-way switch.

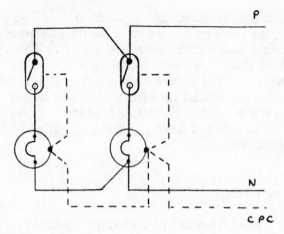

Fig. 7.3 Two lamps controlled by two switches.

(b), or to operate switch two so that its common was in contact with L2. Either of these actions would complete the circuit and the lamp would light.

Intermediate lighting circuits

If it is desired to have control from three or more positions, *intermediate* type switches are necessary as well as the two two-way switches. Intermediate switches have four terminals and although the switch action of different makes of switch end up with the same results, the connections vary, so it is advisable to check the switch action before connecting up. The circuit is wired as shown in drawing (c) of Information Sheet No. 7A; it will be seen that the intermediate switches connect to the two strapping cables. This means that the circuit must always start and finish with the two-way switches. When using the commonest type of intermediate switch for three-way control, the circuit is wired as shown. The switch action in position one is shown with the solid line, and in position two with the dotted line. Operation of the two-way switches is carried out as normal and the lamp can be turned on or off from any of the three positions.

In another often used type, the L1 strappers from the two-way switches are connected into the nearest of the top terminals, but the L2 strappers are taken into the furthest of the bottom terminals (i.e. the cables are crossed over). The switch action in position one is shown and the light is off; position two is shown with a dotted line and in this position the light would be on (see drawing (d)).

Conversion of a one-way circuit into a two-way circuit

On occasions, the electrician is called upon to make alterations to existing circuits. One of the more popular requests is to make a one-way circuit into

Information Sheet No. 7A Two-way and intermediate circuits.

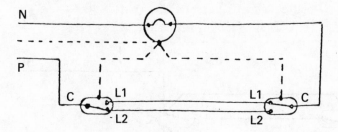

(a) Two-way circuit position one

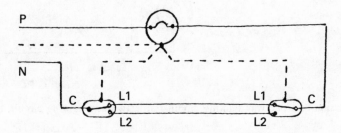

(b) Two-way circuit position two

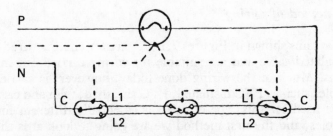

(c) Intermediate circuit type one

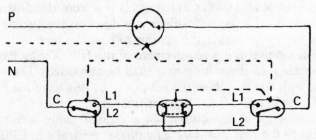

(d) Intermediate circuit type two

a two-way. The conversion can be carried out quite simply by running a piece of three core and CPC cable from the existing switch position to the new position. The connections are made as shown in Fig. 7.4.

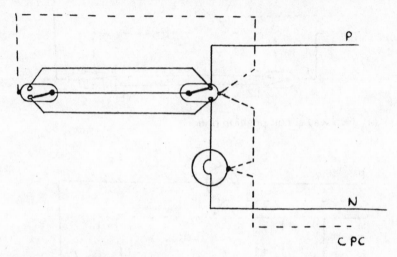

Fig. 7.4 Conversion of a one-way lighting circuit into a two-way lighting circuit.

7.2 Methods of wiring lighting circuits

The loop-in method of wiring

The circuit diagrams shown in Figures 7.1–7.4 are for circuits wired in single core PVC insulated cable and are suitable for wiring carried out in conduit wiring systems. Much of the wiring done today, however, is carried out in composite cables such as PVC insulated, PVC sheathed, twin and earth cable. The technique used for this type of cable is essentially different for that of the singles cables, and the first method we are going to look at is the *loop-in* method.

This is probably the most common method of wiring domestic premises in use today. All the connections are made at the electrical accessories. A cable containing phase neutral and CPC conductors is run from the consumer unit to the first lighting point; a second cable is run down to the switch position. The connections are made inside the ceiling rose at the terminals provided and it should be noted that it is a requirement of the IEE Wiring Regulations that the phase terminal in the ceiling rose shall be shrouded. The reason for this is that, even with the switch in the off position, this terminal is still live until the power is switched off at the consumer unit.

If a further lighting point is required, an additional cable is run from the first lighting point to the new position. The phase, neutral and CPC conductors are connected into the corresponding connections on the first ceiling rose. At the new position, another ceiling rose is fitted and a cable taken down to the new switch position. The connections at the second position are made off in exactly the same way as before, see Fig. 7.5. This procedure is known as looping in and out of the accessories, hence the name *loop-in system*. If any of the current carrying conductors are coloured black, then they must be identified with a red sleeve or piece of red tape, both at the ceiling rose and at the switch.

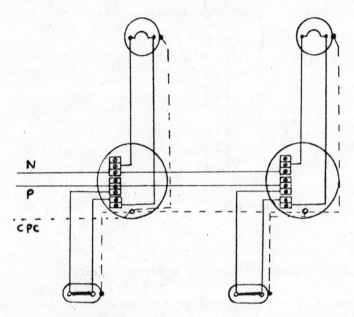

Fig. 7.5 'Loop in' method of wiring.

The joint box method of wiring

There are a number of different types of joint box, but the most popular pattern consists of a circular moulded plastic box in which is fixed four or more brass pillar terminals.

The joint box is sited in a position as near to the centre of the area to be wired as possible, and fixed with wood screws to a suitable timber bearer nailed between the floor or ceiling joists. A composite cable, which contains the phase, neutral and CPC conductors, is run from the consumer unit and terminated in the joint box. Care should be taken to see that the cable sheath enters into the joint box, so no conductors are exposed on the outside. The CPC conductor is bare in composite cables, so it will be necessary to insulate this from the other cables in the joint box. This is done by fitting over it a plastic sleeving, coloured green and yellow in accordance with the IEE Wiring Regulations. To complete the circuit, further cables are run from the light position and the switch position, and the connections are made as shown in Fig. 7.6.

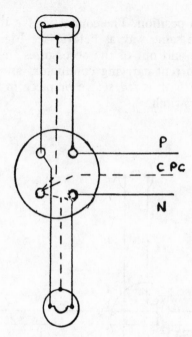

Fig. 7.6 Joint box method of wiring.

7.3 IEE Regulations concerning lighting circuits

We have already seen a number of the regulations applicable to the installation of lighting circuits; however, there are several other points which must be noted.

- Where conductors or flexibles enter a luminaire, as, for example, when a bulkhead fitting or batten lampholder is used, the conductors should be able to withstand any heat likely to be encountered, or sleeved with heat resistant sleeving, Regulation No. 523–3.
- A ceiling rose, unless specially designed for the purpose, should have only one flexible cord, Regulation No. 553–20.
- The flexible cord used to make up a pendant (the ceiling rose, flex and lampholder assembly) should be capable of withstanding any heat that is likely to be present in normal use, Regulation No. 523–1.
- Where a flexible cord supports or partly supports a luminaire, the maximum mass supported shall not exceed the values stated in Regulation No. 523–32.
- A ceiling rose shall not be used on a voltage exceeding 250 V, Regulation No. 553–19.
- Parts of lampholders, installed within 2.5 m of a fixed bath or shower, shall be constructed or shrouded in insulating material. Bayonet-type (B22) lampholders shall be fitted with with a protective shield to BS 5042 (Home Office skirt), or a totally enclosed luminaire installed, Regulation No. 471–38.

- Lighting switches shall be installed, so as to be normally inaccessible to persons using a fixed bath or shower. Regulation No. 471–39. This regulation does not apply to ceiling switches operated by an insulated cord.
- For circuits supplying equipment in a room containing a fixed bath or shower that can be touched at the same time as exposed conductive or extraneous conductive parts, the protective device shall disconnect the circuit within 0.4 of a second, Regulation No. 471–36.
- For circuits on TN or TT systems, where an Edison screw lampholder is being used, the outer contact shall be connected to the neutral conductor, Regulation No. 553–18.
- Final circuits for discharge lighting (this includes fluorescent luminaires) shall be capable of carrying the total steady current, viz the lamp's associated gear and its harmonic currents. Where this information is not available, the demand in volt-amperes can be worked out by multiplying the rated lamp watts by 1.8. This is based on the assumption that the power factor is not less than 0.85 lagging, Appendix 4 of the Regulations.
- Every switch used on discharge lighting (fluorescent luminaires included) shall be designed and marked for that purpose, or shall have a nominal current not less than twice the total steady current it is required to carry. If the final circuit consists of both filament and discharge lighting, then the switch shall have a nominal current not less than the sum of the current of the filament lamps and twice the steady current of the discharge lamps, Regulation No. 537–19.
- Semi-conductors may be used for functional switching (not isolators) provided that they comply with section 512 of the Regulations.
- When installing lighting circuits, the current is equivalent to the connected load with a minimum of 100 W per lampholder, see Table 4 of the Regulations. It should be noted, however, that diversity can be applied to lighting circuits in accordance with Table 4B of the Regulations.

7.4 The installation of 13 A socket outlets

Types of circuit

These circuits supply socket outlets to BS 1363, and permanently connected equipment, via a fused connection unit.

There are two types of circuit listed in Table 5A of the IEE Wiring Regulations for the installation of 13 A socket outlets: (1) the radial final circuit and, (2) the ring final circuit.

(1) The radial final circuit commences at the consumer unit and loops into successive socket outlets, as shown in Fig. 7.7; the circuit ends at the last socket. If the cartridge fuse or circuit breaker, used as an over current protective device, is rated at 30 or 32 A and a minimum conductor size of 4 mm^2 copper, 6 mm^2 copperclad aluminium, or 2.5 mm^2 mineral insulated cable is used, then an unlimited number of socket outlets or fused connection units can be installed in an area not exceeding 50 m^2. In Table 5A of the Regulations, this is classified for description purposes as the A2 circuit.

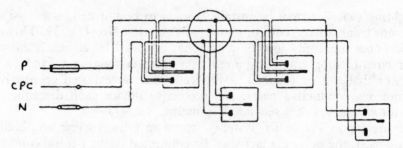

Fig. 7.7 A radial final circuit.

If the radial circuit is protected by any overcurrent device rated at 20 A and a minimum conductor size of 2.5 mm^2 copper, 4 mm^2 copperclad aluminium, or 1.5 mm^2 mineral insulated cable is used, then an unlimited number of socket outlets can be installed in an area of 20 m^2.

In Table 5A this circuit is classified for description purposes as the A3 circuit.

(2) Ring final circuits commence at the consumer unit and loop in and out of successive socket outlets, as shown in Fig. 7.8. The circuit does not end at the final socket as in the radial circuit, but returns back in the form of a ring to the consumer unit. Here it is connected into the same terminals from which it commenced, see Fig. 7.8. In Table 5A this is classified for description purposes as the A1 circuit.

The ring final circuit is protected by any 30 or 32 A rated overcurrent protective device, and should be wired in cables of minimum size 2.5 mm^2 copper, 4 mm^2 copperclad aluminium, or 1.5 mm^2 mineral insulated cable. In an area of 100 m^2, or less, the number of socket outlets or fused connection units is unlimited.

Spurs

A spur is a branch cable connected to a ring or radial final circuit, see Fig. 7.8. These fall into two categories: (1) fused spurs and (2) non-fused spurs.

(1) A fused spur is connected to the circuit through a fused connection unit, the rating of the fuse in the unit not exceeding that of the cable forming the spur, and, in any event, not exceeding 13 A.

(2) Non-fused spurs feed only one single or one twin socket outlet, or one item of permanently connected equipment. Such a spur is connected to the circuit via the terminals of a socket outlet, a spur joint box, or at the origin of the circuit at the consumer unit. The size of the conductor used in non-fused spurs should not be less than that used in the ring.

7.5 IEE Regulations concerning 13 A socket outlets

- For the purposes of Table 5A of the Regulations, each socket outlet of a twin or multiple socket outlet is regarded as one socket outlet.

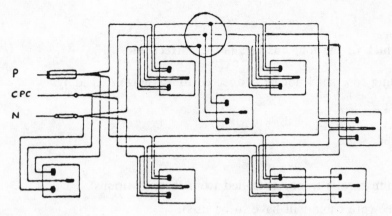

P

CPC

N

Fig. 7.8 A Ring final circuit.

- Diversity between socket outlets and permanently connected equipment has already been taken into account in Table 5A and no further diversity should be applied.
- The cable sizes given are the minimum size and may have to be amended if the circuits are affected by grouping or high ambient temperature, see Appendix 5.
- The total number of fused spurs is unlimited, but the number of non-fused spurs does not exceed the total number of socket outlets and items of stationary equipment connected directly to the circuit.
- The circuit protective conductor is connected in the form of a ring, as shown in Fig. 7.8, except where a metal conduit or enclosure is used as the circuit protective conductor.
- All socket outlets should be protected by a device that will operate in 0.4 seconds.
- No standard 13 A socket should be installed in a room containing a bath.
- Where equipment is to be used outdoors and therefore will be outside the equipotential bonding area, the socket outlet feeding that equipment must be protected by a residual current device with an operating current not exceeding 30 mA.
- All socket outlets feeding equipment as above should carry a label reading 'For Equipment Outdoors'.
- Adjacent sockets should be on the same phase of the supply.

Test 7

Choose which of the four answers is the correct one.

(1) A ceiling rose shall not be connected to a voltage exceeding:

(a) 250 V;
(b) 240 V;
(c) 415 V;
(d) 500 V.

(2) If a luminaire is to be controlled from three positions:

(a) A three core cable will have to be used;
(b) Three two-way switches will be required;
(c) A three gang switch will have to be utilised;
(d) An intermediate switch will have to be used.

(3) The minimum assumed demand for a lighting point is:

(a) 60 W;
(b) 100 W;
(c) 150 W;
(d) 200 W.

(4) All 13 A socket outlets should be protected by:

(a) A protective device that will operate within 0.4 seconds;
(b) A short piece of capping covering the cable connected to it;
(c) A double pole switch;
(d) A single pole switch.

(5) The number of fused spurs allowed on a ring final circuit is:

(a) 12;
(b) Unlimited;
(c) Equal to the number of sockets on the ring;
(d) Less than the number of sockets on the ring.

Chapter 8
The Inspection and Testing of Electrical Installations

8.1 Inspection and testing

Requirements of the IEE Wiring Regulations

Every electrical installation shall be inspected and tested in accordance with the Regulations, before being connected to the public supply. This is to ensure, as far as practicable, that all the requirements of the Regulations have been carried out and the installation is safe to use. The Regulations require that the tests carried out shall not in any way be a danger to persons, property or equipment, even if the circuit is faulty. It is important then that the tests are carried out in the recommended sequence, shown in Part 6 of the Regulations, and this is as follows:

(1) Ring final circuit continuity;
(2) Protective conductor continuity (including all bonding);
(3) Measurement of earth electrode resistance;
(4) Insulation resistance;
(5) Insulation of site built assemblies;
(6) Protection by electrical separation;
(7) Protection by barriers and enclosures;
(8) Insulation of non-conducting floors and walls;
(9) Verification of polarity;
(10) Earth fault loop impedance;
(11) Operation of residual current devices.

Testing final circuits

The testing of electrical installations is an important and skilful job and is best carried out by persons suitably qualified to do so. The above tests will be covered in detail in Books 2 and 3; however, it is not beyond the scope of the beginner to carry out certain of the tests on any final circuits that they might have installed and we shall look at these here.

Visual inspection

Before any of the above tests are carried out, it is a requirement of the Regulations that the installation be visually inspected. Some of the things to look for when carrying out the inspection are as follows:

97

- There should be a notice at the mains intake position, stating that the installation should be regularly inspected and tested;
- Switchgear should be labelled to indicate its purpose;
- There should be warning notices indicating the presence of any voltages exceeding 250 V;
- Circuit charts should be provided indicating the size of cables, protection and load;
- All cables and conductors should be correctly identified;
- Points of connection to the earth electrode and bonding should carry a notice saying 'Safety Electrical Connection – Do Not Remove';
- Sockets to be used for equipment outside the equipotential bonding zone should have a notice saying 'For Equipment Outdoors';
- Equipment should be checked to see if it complies with British Standards;
- Ensure that no electronic equipment is in the circuit as this could be damaged by the test;
- Check that the protective system, including bonding, is in place as some of the tests carried out later are at mains potential and could otherwise prove dangerous;
- A check should be made to see that good workmanship and proper materials have been used in accordance with Regulation 13–1;
- Correct the choice and setting of protective and monitoring devices;
- All equipment should be erected, installed, connected and protected to comply with the fundamental requirements for safety, as listed in Chapter 13 of the Regulations and Chapter 3 of this book.

Continuity of ring final circuit conductors

The Regulations state that the continuity of all conductors (including protective conductors) of every final ring circuit should be tested for continuity. There are two methods of carrying this out, as follows:

Method one

Take the two ends of the phase conductor of the ring final circuit before connection is made into the distribution board. Using an ohmmeter or selecting ohms on your insulation tester, measure the continuity resistance and note its value; call this reading A.

After connecting the two ends of the phase conductors together, a second reading is made between this terminal and the phase terminal of a socket on the ring final circuit, which is nearest to the mid point of the circuit. A note is made of the second reading and, if a long lead has been used to reach the mid point; then its resistance should be measured and taken away from the second reading; call this reading B. The resulting value of reading B should be one quarter of reading A. This should be repeated for neutral and circuit protective conductors; see Information Sheet No. 8A.

Method two

The resistance between the open ends of phase, neutral and circuit protective conductors is taken as before and a note made of their resistance; call this reading A.

Information Sheet No. 8A Testing ring final circuits – Method 1.

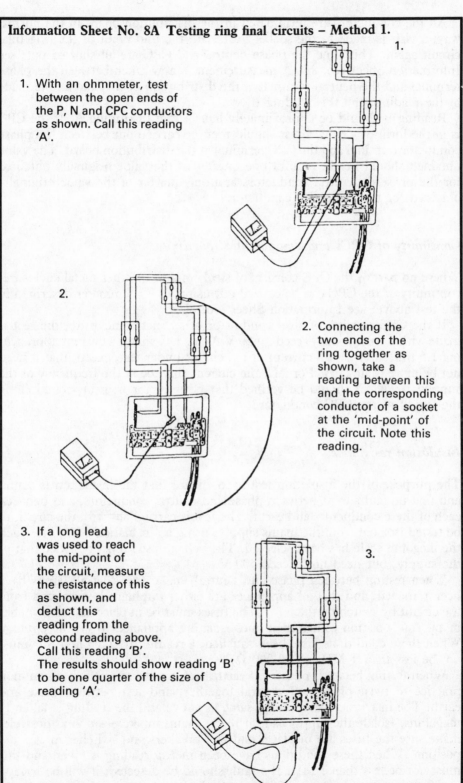

1. With an ohmmeter, test between the open ends of the P, N and CPC conductors as shown. Call this reading 'A'.

2. Connecting the two ends of the ring together as shown, take a reading between this and the corresponding conductor of a socket at the 'mid-point' of the circuit. Note this reading.

3. If a long lead was used to reach the mid-point of the circuit, measure the resistance of this as shown, and deduct this reading from the second reading above. Call this reading 'B'. The results should show reading 'B' to be one quarter of the size of reading 'A'.

All the conductors are terminated in the distribution board in the normal way; a visit is made to the socket nearest to the mid point of the ring final circuit again. This time the phase neutral and CPC are all shorted out; see Information Sheet No. 8B. A measurement is now taken between the phase terminal and the neutral terminal at the distribution board, and a note made of the reading; call this reading B.

Reading B should be approximately half of that of reading A. If the CPC is in the form of a ring, a test should then be carried out between the phase conductor terminal and the CPC terminal at the distribution board. The value obtained should be the sum of one quarter of the value originally obtained for the phase or neutral conductors and one quarter of the value originally obtained for the protective conductor.

Continuity of CPCs and equipotential bonding

Where no part of the CPC consists of steel conduit or other metal enclosure, continuity of the CPC can be carried out using a DC ohmmeter described in the test above; see Information Sheet No. 8C.

If the CPC consists of steel conduit or other metal enclosure, the test is made with a voltage not exceeding 50 V AC or DC and at a current approaching 1.5 times the design current of the circuit under test, except that it need not be more than 25 A. For AC, the current shall be at the frequency of the supply. If DC, it should be verified that no inductor is incorporated along the length of the CPC conductor.

Insulation resistance

The purpose of the insulation test is to ensure that the insulation is sound and that no faults exist between phase and neutral conductors, and between each of these conductors and earth. The test is carried out with the circuit to be tested isolated from the mains supply, using an insulation tester on which the megohm scale has been selected. The voltage used must be twice that of the supply, but need not exceed 500 V.

When testing between phase and neutral, make sure that all lamps have been removed, and that all appliances are either unplugged or isolated from the circuit by switching them off. The fuses must be in place and all switches in the 'on' position (other than ones isolating appliances from the circuit). When these conditions have been satisfied, a reading is taken and this must not be less than 1 MΩ (1 000 000 Ω).

When testing between phase and earth, and neutral to earth, it is common practice to twist phase and neutral together, and test between these and earth. The instrument used is the same as above and the reading is taken in megohms. Isolate the supply as near to the mains intake position as possible; make sure the fuses are in place, and any breakers and switches in the 'on' position. When these conditions have been met, a reading is taken and this must not be less than 1 MΩ. If a fault should be detected, it will be necessary to test between phase and earth, and neutral and earth separately, in

Information Sheet No. 8B Testing ring final circuits – Method 2.

1.

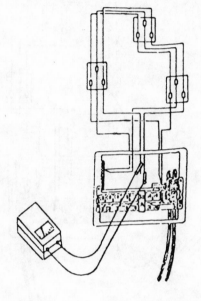

1. Measure between the open ends of each of the conductors. Note the reading and call it reading 'A'.

2.

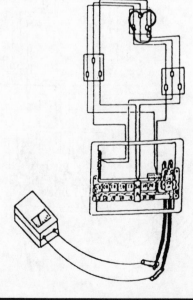

2. Connect the conductors into the CU and with the mid-point of the circuit shorted as shown take a reading between phase and neutral. Call this 'B'. 'B' should be about half the value of reading 'A'. A further test between phase and CPC should give a value of one quarter.

Information Sheet No. 8C Polarity and continuity tests.

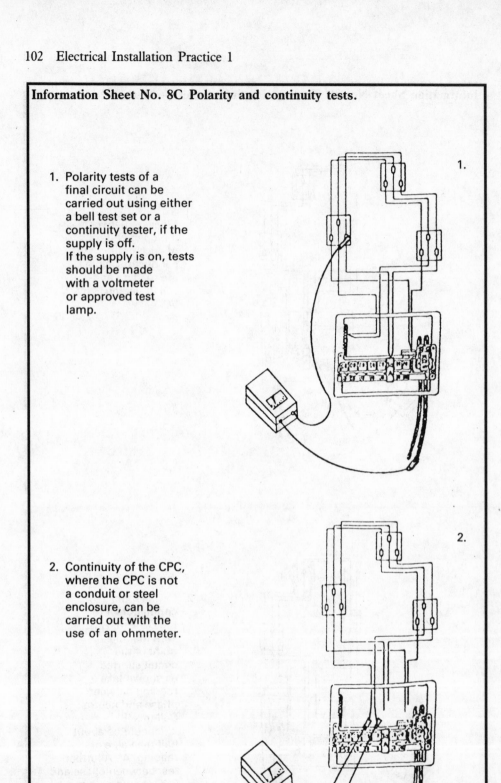

1. Polarity tests of a
   final circuit can be
   carried out using either
   a bell test set or a
   continuity tester, if the
   supply is off.
   If the supply is on, tests
   should be made
   with a voltmeter
   or approved test
   lamp.

2. Continuity of the CPC,
   where the CPC is not
   a conduit or steel
   enclosure, can be
   carried out with the
   use of an ohmmeter.

Information Sheet No. 8D Insulation testing.

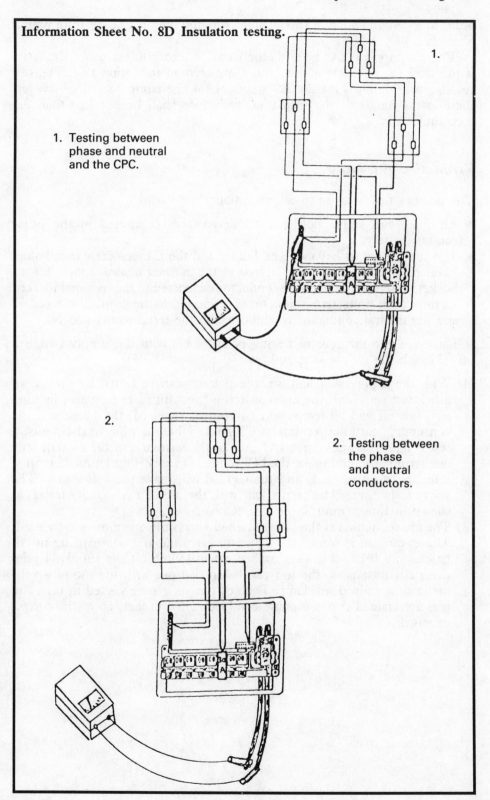

1. Testing between phase and neutral and the CPC.

2. Testing between the phase and neutral conductors.

order to ascertain which of these conductors the fault is on; see Information Sheet No. 8D.

Where equipment has been disconnected in order to carry out the tests, if practical the equipment itself must undergo an insulation test. The test result must comply with the BS standard for the equipment, if, however, there is no standard, the insulation resistance shall be not less than 0.5 megohms.

Verification of polarity

The polarity test is made to establish that:

- All fuses and single pole control devices are connected in the phase conductor only;
- The centre contact bayonet lampholder and the Edison-screw lampholder have their outer contacts connected to the earthed neutral conductor;
- Socket outlets have the phase conductor connected to the terminal marked L; the circuit protective conductor is connected to the terminal marked E, and the neutral conductor is connected to the terminal marked N.

There are two methods of testing polarity, (1) with the supply switched off, (2) with the supply switched on.

(1) With the supply switched off, the polarity can be tested by the use of a bell test set. With the main switch off, circuit fuses in place, lighting switches off and all lamps and equipment removed, the phase and the consumer's earthing terminal are linked. When lighting final circuits, a test is made between earth and each of the terminals of the switch; only one terminal should make the bell sound. On socket outlet final circuits, a test between phase L and the CPC E will make the bell sound. The above tests can also be carried out with the use of a continuity tester, as shown in Information Sheet No. 8C.

(2) The above method is the safest method and is the one most widely used. The electrician is sometimes asked to carry out tests on existing instal-lations and it is not always convenient to switch off the supply. Under these circumstances, the test can be carried out with the use of a volt-meter or approved test lamp. Each of the outlets are visited in turn and it is ascertained that the phase conductors do, in fact, go to the correct terminals.

Test 8

Choose which of the four answers is the correct one.

(1) The sequence of testing an installation is important because:

(a) It saves time switching the supply on and off;
(b) Tests dependent on one another are in the correct order;
(c) It saves changing the meter over to another scale;
(d) Time is saved changing to different meters.

(2) The insulation resistance between phase and neutral must not:

(a) Be less than 1 megohm;
(b) Be more than 1 megohm;
(c) Be read in megohms;
(d) Be on the infinity mark.

(3) A polarity test is carried out to see that:

(a) The circuit works correctly before connection to the supply;
(b) All current carrying conductors are coloured red;
(c) The CPC is continuous throughout its length;
(d) All single pole devices are connected in the phase conductor.

(4) The continuity of a ring final circuit is checked with:

(a) An earth loop impedance tester;
(b) An insulation tester switched to the megohm scale;
(c) An earth electrode resistance tester;
(d) An insulation tester switched to the ohm scale.

(5) If the CPC is a steel conduit or enclosure, the test current:

(a) Must be 1.5 times the design current, up to a maximum of 25 A;
(b) Must be equal to the design current of the circuit;
(c) Must be less than the design current of the circuit;
(d) Must be 1.8 times the design current, up to a maximum of 25 A.

Chapter 9
The Installation of Bells and Secondary Cells

9.1 The installation of electric bells (sounders)

Electric bells

When an electric current flows through a conductor, a magnetic field is created around the conductor. If the conductor takes the form of a coil of wire wound round a soft iron core, the core becomes a magnet due to the influence of the magnetic field.

This arrangement, which is known as an electromagnet or solenoid, is the basis of the electric bell. Most electric bells have two electromagnets, a gong and a strip of soft iron, called an armature, which is supported by a spring and carries a striker.

Single stroke bell

In this the simplest type of bell, the coils of the electromagnets are connected to two terminals mounted on the base of the bell. The wiring from the source of electricity (generally a small mains transformer or internal batteries) is taken through a one–way push directly to the bell's terminals.

When the push is pressed, the circuit is completed and current flows from the source across the push contacts, through the electromagnet coils and back to the other pole of the source. A magnetic field is created around the coils, so that the soft iron cores become magnetised and attract the soft iron armature. Because the magnetism is stronger than the spring attached to the armature, the armature moves towards the electromagnets and the striker or hammer which is attached to the armature hits the gong.

As soon as the push is released, there is a break in the circuit and the current no longer flows. There is then no current in the coils and therefore no magnetic field is created, so the armature is no longer attracted and is pulled back into its original position by the action of the spring.

This type of bell, as its name implies, gives one stroke of the gong each time that the push is pressed. It is often used in signalling systems (those between passengers and bus driver, for example) and for circuits where two or more bells have to operate in series (see Information Sheet No. 9A).

Trembler bells

The common domestic or commercial door bell is generally known as the trembler bell. Although similar in most respects to the single stroke bell, it is

Information Sheet No. 9A Types of bell.

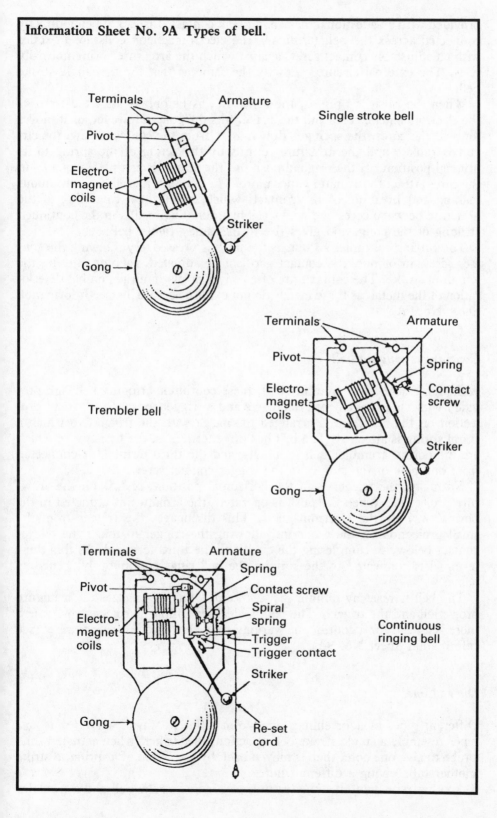

Single stroke bell

Terminals
Armature
Pivot
Electro-magnet coils
Striker
Gong

Trembler bell

Terminals
Armature
Pivot
Spring
Electro-magnet coils
Contact screw
Striker
Gong

Continuous ringing bell

Terminals
Armature
Spring
Pivot
Contact screw
Spiral spring
Electro-magnet coils
Trigger
Trigger contact
Striker
Gong
Re-set cord

provided with an additional make and break contact. Instead of being directly connected across the bell terminals, the electromagnetic coils are in series with an adjustable contact screw against which the armature spring normally rests. The external circuit is exactly the same as that for the single stroke bell.

When the push is pressed, the armature, as before, is attracted towards the electromagnetic cores and the striker hits the gong. However, as it moves towards the cores, the spring is drawn away from the contact screw, the circuit is broken and the armature returns by the action of the spring to its original position. In the original position, the circuit is completed again and the cores attract the armature once more. The action is therefore a continuous making and breaking of the contact, which results in a trembling of the armature between cores and contact. This trembling results in the continued striking of the gong, and gives rise to its name *trembler* bell.

The ringing continues as long as the push is pressed. By screwing the contact screw in or out, the contact gap can be adjusted, thereby altering the length of stroke. The contacts are often silver or platinum to combat deterioration of the metal, as these metals do not oxidise very easily (see Information Sheet No. 9A).

Continuous ringing bell

Although essentially a trembler bell, these continuous ringing bells are provided with an arrangement of contacts and a trigger, or catch. A small projection on the armature is arranged to engage with the trigger, to which a spiral spring is attached. The bell has three terminals, the first two of which are the normal trembler bell terminals, and the third terminal is connected from one pole of the supply to the trigger contact screw.

Normally, the trigger is in the horizontal position, resting on the armature projection. When the push is operated, the armature is attracted in the normal way by the electromagnets. This disengages the trigger from the small projection on the armature, allowing the trigger to touch the trigger contact below, so completing the circuit to the third terminal. As this third terminal is connected to the supply, the bell rings continuously, hence its name.

The bell is reset by pulling the *reset cord*, which re-engages the armature projection and the trigger. The bell is ideal for simple alarm systems, where there is a need for a continuous warning until the system is safe to reset (see Information Sheet No. 9A).

Door chimes

Different types of door chimes operate in different ways. Some *double note* types resemble a single stroke bell in action; the striker, when actuated, hits a tube to give one note, then is moved back by the action of a spring to strike another tube giving a different note.

Another type combines the features of a single stroke bell and a trembler bell. By this means, three distinctive types of chime can be obtained. For example, a continuous chime for the front door, a double note for the back door and a single note for a third door or internal call signal. This type of chime usually has a mercury switch to provide the trembler action.

There is yet another type, operated by a synchronous motor and having a volume control, which plays the eight-note tune of the Westminster Chimes.

Buzzers

For some purposes, although an audible warning is required, the rather strident tones of a bell are not suitable. Or it may be that a bell is already installed for some other purpose, say a fire alarm system. In cases like this, an alternative sound to the bell is required and a buzzer is often installed.

Buzzers work on exactly the same principle as trembler bells, except that they have no hammer and no gong. The characteristic buzzing is provided by the vibration of the contact breaker movement.

They can be obtained with different pitches. For a high pitched note, the mechanism is as light as possible. In addition, a certain amount of variation is provided by the adjustment of the contact screw (see Fig. 9.1).

Bell pushes and contacts

Different types of bell pushes are made for various situations. For outside use, brass barrel type pushes are most serviceable as the contacts, operated through a spiral spring, are totally enclosed in a brass tube, which is usually let into the wall or door frame. Various surface mounting types can be obtained; these are mostly made of plastic and can be obtained in various shapes and colours. Some of these have space for the householder's name and are illuminated by a small lamp, while others glow in the dark so that they are easily seen. Multi-gang pushes are available for use in flats and they too have space for the flat owner's name. The majority of these pushes have contacts,

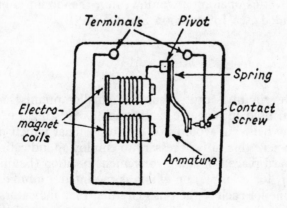

Fig. 9.1 Buzzer.

which rely on the springiness of sheet brass, and are operated by direct pressure of the finger on a push button (see Fig. 9.2).

Contacts to give audible warning to shopkeepers, when customers enter the shop, are arranged either at the top of the door, so that the contacts are closed by the opening of the door, or on the floor, so that treading on the mat or floor-board closes the contacts. There are several different types, with steel springs, phosphor bronze springs, ball contact or brackets.

Bell circuits

The simplest bell circuit is, of course, one in which a bell, a push, and a source of supply are connected in series. To operate the bell independently from other positions, additional pushes would have to be wired in parallel with the original push. If further bells are required, it is only necessary to wire these in parallel with the existing bell (see Fig. 9.3).

Bell circuits are used for many warning and alarm systems, one of the most popular is the *intruder alarm*. These circuits may be broadly classified into two groups: (1) open circuit – in which the contacts in the circuit are normally open, and (2) closed circuit – in which the contacts in the circuit are normally closed.

The open circuit is the more common. In this case, opening a window or door causes the closing of the contacts which energise the bell. It has the advantage that current flows in the circuit only when the contacts are closed. A key switch is included in the circuit, so that the occupants of the premises can open the windows or doors in the daytime without ringing the alarm bell. The main disadvantage of this type of circuit is that it can be rendered useless by cutting the wiring.

In a closed circuit, a small current flows continuously through the normally closed contacts in the circuit and energises the coil of a relay, or automatic switch. The contacts of the relay are held open by this current, preventing the bell circuit from being energised. On opening a window or door, the circuit is broken; no current then flows through the coil of the relay and the contacts of the relay close. This completes the bell circuit and the alarm is sounded. The advantage of the closed circuit system is that if a wire is cut, it has the same effect as opening a window, i.e., the circuit is broken and the alarms are sounded (see Information Sheet No. 9B).

Indicating boards

While the above circuit is quite useful in smaller premises, it has certain drawbacks when used in bigger establishments. Pressing any of the pushes would sound the bell, but would not tell the listener which push had been operated. To achieve this, it is necessary to employ an indicating board. This consists of a board placed in some convenient position (behind the porter's desk in an hotel, for example) on which is mounted a number of indicating lights or flags, one for each of the push circuits. Flag indicators (see Fig. 9.4) have been used for many years and there are a number of different types.

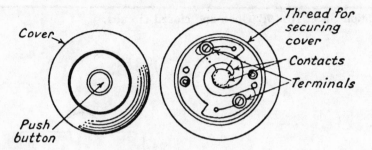

Fig. 9.2 Bell push.

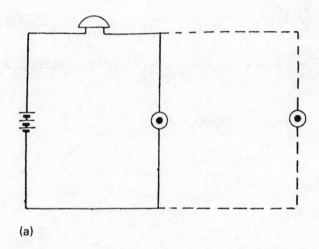

(a)

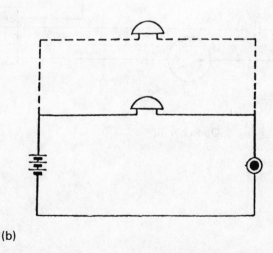

(b)

Fig. 9.3 Bell circuit – additional bell. (a) Additional push; (b) Additional bell.

Information Sheet No. 9B Open and closed circuits.

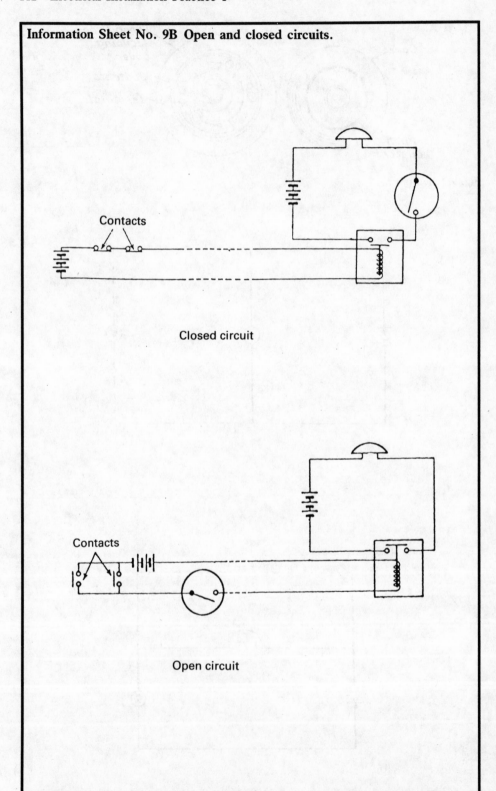

Closed circuit

Open circuit

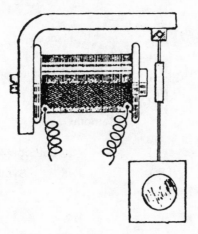

Fig. 9.4 Flag indicator.

The simplest operates in a similar way to that of the single stroke bell, but carries a flag on the armature instead of a striker. When the push is operated, the electromagnet is energised and attracts the flag carrying armature. When the push is released, the armature drops back and continues to swing like a pendulum, thus indicating which push has been operated.

These are now being replaced by indicating boards with indicator lights on them, many of which are electronically operated and use *light emitting diodes* (LEDs) as a means of indication (see Fig. 9.5). A LED is made from the semi-conducting compound *gallium arsenide phosphate*, and emits light when it is *forward biased*; that is when the electrons flow across the device in a certain way. This causes a rise in temperature in most semi-conductor materials and in gallium arsenide phosphate, some of the energy is given off as light. The colour of the LED depends on the composition and purity of the compound; at present only red, yellow and green colours are available. A LED does not light on reverse bias and, in fact, the device can be damaged if this is attempted. It is essential, therefore, that when testing any electrical circuit that may contain electronic devices, that these are disconnected during the test to avoid damage.

9.2 Regulations affecting the installation of bell circuits

Bell circuits, or any extra-low voltage circuits that are fed from a safety source complying with IEE Regulation No. 411–3, do not come within the scope of these Regulations. However, the transformer and equipment associated with these do; also, if the wiring is in contact in any way with the cables of low voltage circuits, when it too should comply with the requirements of the Regulations regarding segregation.

The bell transformer should be mounted as close to the customer's switch-gear as possible, and protected by its own 5 A fuse or circuit breaker. The wiring to the primary side of the transformer from the mains supply must comply in every way with the IEE Wiring Regulations, with regard to size

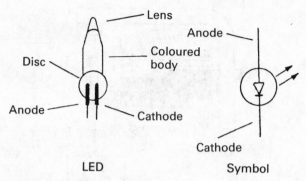

Fig. 9.5 Light Emitting Diode (LED).

and its installation. The wiring from the secondary side of the transformer, which is carried out under normal circumstances with bell wire, does not come under the scope of the Regulations; however, it should be carried out with the same care and attention as if it did.

Segregation of circuits

Circuits in electrical installations are split up into three categories:

Category 1 – All low voltage circuits (except fire alarms and emergency lighting);
Category 2 – Extra low voltage i.e. telephone, sound, bell and call systems (except fire alarms and emergency lighting);
Category 3 – Fire alarms and emergency lighting.

Category 1 circuits cannot be drawn into the same conduit or trunking as category 2 circuits, unless the latter are wired in cables insulated in accordance with the Regulations to the highest category 1 voltage present.

Cables of category 1 shall not, under any circumstances, be drawn into the same conduit or trunking as category 3 cables. The only exception to this is if the category 3 circuit was wired in mineral insulated cable.

There are several special circumstances other than those mentioned above and these can be found in Regulation 525–1 to 525–9.

From this it will be seen that bell circuits must not be drawn into the same conduit or trunking as the mains voltage cables. The exception to this would be if you wired your bell circuit in cables having the same standard of insulation as your mains voltage cables.

9.3 Care and maintenance of secondary cells

Secondary cells

Secondary cells, unlike primary cells, are not a primary source of electricity supply. They merely store the energy, and need to be charged by the application of an external supply before they can be used. Their current output capability, when connected together in the form of a battery, is much greater than primary cells, often exceeding 100 A, for example, when starting a car.

Secondary cells are rated in ampere hours (Ah). This is a measure of the amount of electricity they can store and the time taken to discharge it. For example, a battery rated at 60 Ah would give a steady current of 6 A for 10 hours before the voltage dropped below an acceptable level (say 1.85 V). The same battery would give a continuous current of 10 A for six hours.

Types of secondary cell

These fall into two main categories: (1) ones using acid as a basis for their electrolyte, known as *lead-acid cells* and (2) ones using alkaline, known as *alkaline cells*.

(1) In lead-acid cells, the positive and the negative plates are made of lead and the electrolyte is dilute sulphuric acid, hence the name lead-acid. The whole assembly is placed in an acid resistant container, with positive and negative plates alternating with each other. The plates are kept apart by acid resistant separators of ebonite or special plastic formers. The plates can be of two types: (a) formed type, in which the plates undergo a charging and discharging process, causing the negative plates to be covered in *spongy lead* and the positive plate to be covered in *lead peroxide*. This is an expensive operation and cheaper cells often use (b) pasted plates. These are in the form of a grid, in which is pressed a compound of sulphuric acid and red lead. Care must be taken not to charge or discharge this type of plate too rapidly or they buckle and loosen the paste filling.

(2) There are two types of alkaline cell, the nickel iron and the nickel cadmium. In the nickel iron cell the positive plate is made of *nickel hydroxide* and the negative plate of *iron oxide*. In the nickel cadmium cell, the positive plate is also nickel hydroxide; however, the negative plate is made of cadmium with a small amount of iron. The electrolyte for both types is potassium hydroxide. The plates for alkaline cells consist of flat nickel steel grids for the negative plates and either flat nickel steel grids or thin cylindrical tubes for the positive plates. These plates contain the active chemicals and are insulated from each other by ebonite rods; the whole assembly is placed in a welded steel container. As the construction of alkaline cells is for the most part steel, this gives the cells great mechanical strength; despite this they remain lighter than the lead-acid cells, see Fig. 9.6.

Care and maintenance of lead-acid cells

If these cells are regularly maintained, there is no reason why they should not last for many years. The level of the electrolyte should never be allowed to fall below the level of the tops of the plates; some cells have marks on the

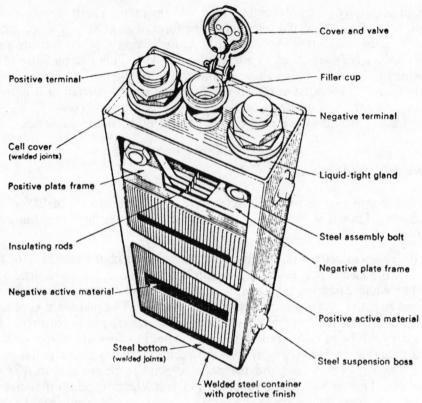

Positive terminal

Cover and valve

Filler cup

Negative terminal

Cell cover
(welded joints)

Positive plate frame

Liquid-tight gland

Insulating rods

Steel assembly bolt

Negative plate frame

Negative active material

Positive active material

Steel bottom
(welded joints)

Steel suspension boss

Welded steel container
with protective finish

Fig. 9.6 Alkaline cell.

case to indicate this level. If the electrolyte does fall, then it can be topped up using distilled water. Tap water should not be used, as this often contains impurities that will shorten the life of your battery. If, for some reason, spillage takes place, this can be washed down with water containing soda. When mixing fresh electrolyte, always add acid to the distilled water, not distilled water to the acid, otherwise there will be a violent reaction and someone could be injured. Rubber gloves should be worn during this operation, together with an acid resistant apron or overall. If large quantities are involved, eye protection of some kind should be employed. This could take the form of a protective screen or goggles.

When the lead-acid cell begins to discharge, the electrolyte becomes weaker and its specific gravity drops. This can be measured by the use of an hydrometer (see Information Sheet No. 9C), which consists of a glass syringe containing a specially weighted float. The flexible nozzle of the hydrometer is placed into the cell, the bulb at the other end depressed and acid allowed to be drawn into the glass syringe. The float has a graduated scale and readings can be taken off; the higher the float is above the level of the electrolyte, the higher will be the specific gravity. For a fully charged lead-acid cell, the reading should be 1.28; this will drop to a level of 1.18 when discharged and is a good indication of the level of charge of a cell. The colour of the plates is anther good indicator of the state of charge of this type of cell. In its fully

Information Sheet No. 9C Hydrometer.

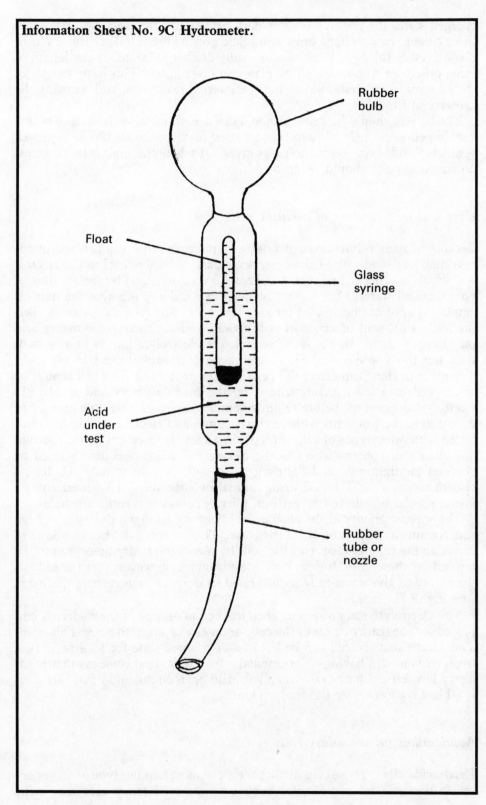

Rubber
bulb

Float

Glass
syringe

Acid
under
test

Rubber
tube or
nozzle

charged state, the positive plate is dark brown and the negative plate grey; these colours pale to light brown and pale grey as the cell discharges. Never allow a cell of this type to remain in a fully discharged state for any length of time, otherwise sulphation of the plates will take place. This coats the plates with a layer of sulphate, increasing the internal resistance, and reducing the capacity of the cell.

The battery should be kept clean and dry and all metalwork covered with a coat of petroleum jelly. Rooms that are used for batteries should be kept well ventilated and, because of the gases given off when charging is in progress, no smoking rules should be enforced.

Care and maintenance of alkaline cells

Because of their robust construction, alkaline cells require much less attention than lead-acid cells. Like other secondary cells, the level of the electrolyte should be checked regularly and any losses made good by the addition of pure distilled water. Care should be taken when doing this that the utensils employed have not been used on lead-acid cells. The contamination of alkaline cells with acid of any sort will seriously affect their performance and may destroy them. If, for some reason, the electrolyte has to be renewed, then only the type specified by the manufacturer should be used, as any slight difference in these can affect the performance of the cell. The cell should be discharged to a level recommended by the manufacturers and all the old electrolyte drained off before refilling commences. With this type of cell, we do not have the problems with corrosive fumes and electrolyte splashes associated with other types of cell, though cleanliness is more important to avoid any chance of contamination of the electrolyte. All connections should be checked for tightness, and lightly greased with petroleum jelly. Under no circumstances should grease using animal or vegetable fat be used and no grease should be allowed to get into filler openings or ventilation holes.

The specific gravity of the alkaline cell does not go down during discharge and remains at a level of 1.2 during use. This means that the technique of checking the state of charge of the cell, by use of the hydrometer, cannot be utilised for these cells. It does have the advantage, however, that the cell has the ability to give practically its full rated capacity at high rates of discharge (see Fig. 9.7).

The electrolyte has no serious chemical action on any of the materials employed for the construction of the cell, or on any of the active materials used. This means that the cell can be left in a discharged state for long periods of time, without this having a detrimental effect on it. It also means that it has a very low self-discharge rate when left in an open circuit situation; this gives it a big advantage over the lead-acid cell.

Applications for secondary cells

Lead-acid cells   These cells are probably the most familiar type of secondary cell in use. Almost every motor vehicle on the road today uses one for its

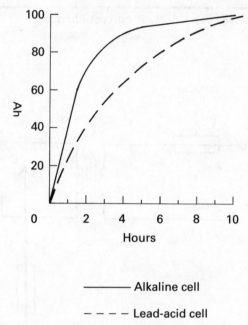

Fig. 9.7 Discharge rates of alkaline and lead-acid cells.

electrical system. Six of the cells are used together to form a 12 V battery. They are relatively inexpensive, can produce the high current necessary for the starting of a car and have a high discharge voltage. They are not as robust as other types of secondary cell, however, and do require regular mainten-ance. They are often used for standby supplies, and emergency lighting and fire alarm systems.

Alkaline cells   More costly than lead-acid cells, nine of these cells are re-quired to form a 12 V battery. Because they are very robust, can be charged and discharged quickly without damage, and left for long periods in a dis-charged state, they are often used in vehicles and equipment used by the armed forces. They are ideal for marine use and where expense is not a major consideration, they are being used more and more for standby supplies.

The charging of secondary cells

The charging of secondary cells is carried out by connecting them to some sort of regulated DC supply. This is usually a rectified AC supply, although it could be by means of a DC mains, a DC generator or a rotary converter. There are three commonly used methods of achieving this: (1) constant cur-rent charging, (2) constant voltage charging, and (3) trickle charging.

(1) In this method, the charge is begun at what is known as the starting cur-rent. This is continued until the voltage reaches a point some 20% above the cells' fully charged emf (exact figures should be obtained from the

Information Sheet No. 9D Constant current charging.

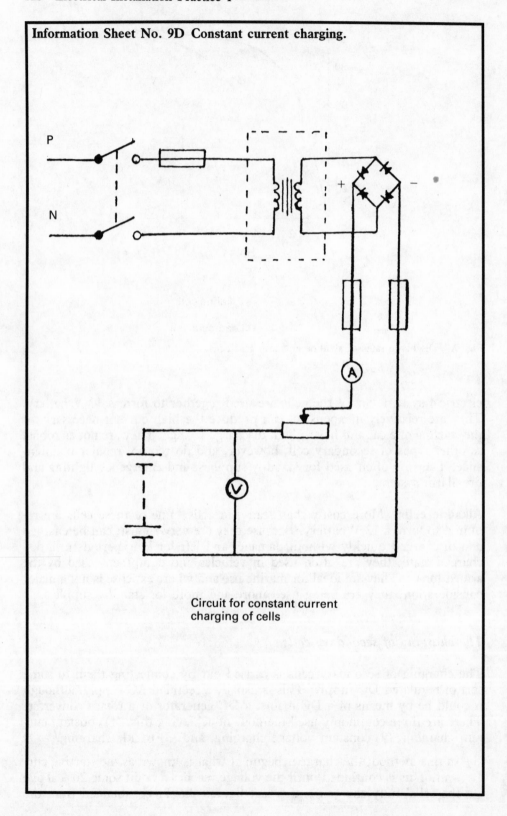

Circuit for constant current
charging of cells

Information Sheet No. 9E Constant voltage charging.

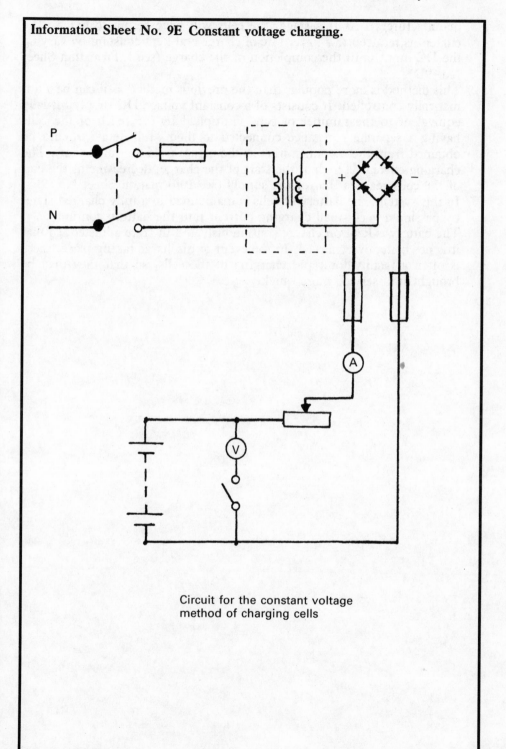

Circuit for the constant voltage
method of charging cells

manufacturers). At this stage, the cells will have begun to *gas*, so the current is reduced to a lower rate of charge and kept constant by varying the DC input until the completion of the charge (see Information Sheet No. 9D).

(2) This method is more popular than the previous method as it can be automatically controlled. It consists of a constant voltage DC supply, usually equivalent to the number of cells multiplied by 2.6, each of the cells having a separate resistance connected to them (full details should be obtained from the manufacturers as the values used are important). The charging current is high at the start of the charge, decreasing as the emf of the cells reaches that of the supply (see Information Sheet No. 9E).

(3) In this system, the battery of cells is maintained in a fully charged state, by passing a very small charging current into the battery continuously. The battery is kept on charge continuously and the rate adjusted, so that it is not being overcharged. In the event of discharge taking place, there is often a facility for rapid charging of the cells, so that they may be brought into service more quickly.

Test 9

Choose which of the four answers is the correct one.

(1) In an open circuit system, the pushes are connected:

(a) In series with each other;
(b) In parallel with each other;
(c) In parallel with the bell;
(d) Across the supply.

(2) Bell circuits fed from a safety source of extra low voltage are classified as:

(a) Category 2 circuits;
(b) Category 3 circuits;
(c) Low voltage circuits;
(d) High voltage circuits.

(3) If the pushes in a bell circuit are connected in series it is:

(a) An open circuit;
(b) A short circuit;
(c) A radial circuit;
(d) A closed circuit.

(4) The positive plate of a fully charged lead-acid cell is:

(a) Coloured pale grey;
(b) Coloured dark brown;
(c) Made of white lead;
(d) Made of mercuric oxide.

(5) The electrolyte of a alkaline cell is a solution of:

(a) Potassium hydroxide;
(b) Sodium hydroxide;
(c) Potassium chlorate;
(d) Acetic acid.

Answers to the Tests

Test 1

(1) (b);   (2) (a);   (3) (c);   (4) (d);   (5) (a).

Test 2

(1) (c);   (2) (d);   (3) (b);   (4) (c);   (5) (d).

Test 3

(1) (d);   (2) (d);   (3) (a);   (4) (b);   (5) (c).

Test 4

(1) (d);   (2) (c);   (3) (a);   (4) (b);   (5) (d).

Test 5

(1) (c);   (2) (c);   (3) (a);   (4) (b);   (5) (d).

Test 6

(1) (b);   (2) (a);   (3) (b);   (4) (c);   (5) (d).

Test 7

(1) (a);   (2) (d);   (3) (b);   (4) (a);   (5) (b).

Test 8

(1) (b);   (2) (a);   (3) (d);   (4) (d);   (5) (a).

Test 9

(1) (b);   (2) (a);   (3) (d);   (4) (b);   (5) (a).

Index